Star-Studded Service

SIX STEPS TO WINNING
PATIENT SATISFACTION

* * * * *

KEVIN W. SULLIVAN

MERYL D. LUALLIN

Medical Group
Management
Association
MGMA®

Medical Group Management Association
104 Inverness Terrace East
Englewood, CO 80112-5306
877.275.6462
Website: www.mgma.com

Production Credits
Editorial Director: Marilee E. Aust
Manuscript Review: Marti A. Cox, MLIS
Page Design, Composition, and Production: Boulder Bookworks, LLC
Copy Editor: Mara Gaiser
Proofreader: Scott Vickers
Cover: Ian Serff, Serff Creative Group, Inc.

Item #: 6635

ISBN-13: 978-1-56829-281-6

* * * * *

ACKNOWLEDGEMENTS/DEDICATION

To the Customer Service team at Sullivan/Luallin

"The service we render is the rent we pay

for our room on the earth."

SIR WILLIAM GRENFELL

* * *

Contents

Appendices

Introduction

*A visitor to Mother Teresa's hospice in the
Calcutta slums marveled at the selflessness of the
nuns who labored over homeless, terminally ill men.
Passing a young novice gently toweling the
whitened skin of a man in the final stages
of leprosy, the visitor whispered to his host
"I wouldn't do that for a million dollars."*

*The young woman looked up, smiling.
"Neither would I," she said.*

HEALING IS THE SCIENCE OF MEDICINE; SERVICE IS ITS HEART.

Caring for people is what drew you to the world of healing, whether you practice medicine or support those who do. You accept the pressure and the extra-step hassle that makes you drag yourself home each evening, as long as you can feel that you've made a difference in someone's life.

Yet the "service" mission is getting harder to live up to these days. Unpredictable patient volume, unanticipated work-ins, ringing telephones, variability in patient expectations, lean staffing and limited resources – the multiple challenges of today's medical environment – can cause even the most dedicated professionals to "retreat to process" to get through the workday.

At the same time, health plans and other payers are placing a higher premium on patient satisfaction as a primary measure of quality. They field longer and more detailed surveys to ask how members feel about their encounters with physicians and the employees they meet during their visit. More than ever, the findings are used to identify "preferred" providers and reward top scorers with "pay for performance" incentives.

This is a book about service – or, more to the point, how to meet the service expectations of patients and caregivers while preserving the fulfillment and career enthusiasm you expected when you entered the medical field.

Kahlil Gibran said that only "when you have reached the mountain top, then you shall begin to climb." This book is dedicated to all those who have chosen a career in medicine – you may manage a department, a clinic, or a multi-tiered delivery system, but for you, the climb never ends. You belong to an elite group of climbers who know that medicine is not medicine if it separates the person from the pathology.

Into these chapters are packed more than 20 years of observations derived from working with small and large practices in nearly every U.S. marketplace. To illustrate our conclusions, you'll encounter the real-life accounts of people who walk where you walk and meet the same challenges that make your life both interesting and difficult.

We sincerely hope that what we've learned will be of value to you.

KEVIN W. SULLIVAN   MERYL D. LUALLIN

PART ONE

MARKETING BASICS

WHAT IS PRACTICE MARKETING?

In the Marcus Welby days – when solo-practice doctors were revered and house calls were a hallmark of family medicine – marketing a medical practice amounted to little more than hanging a shingle, joining a few civic organizations, and making friends on the local hospital medical staff.

It's all different now. Physicians work together in groups, and practice efficiency requires delivery systems where patients come to the doctor for care. Health plans and self-insured employers have intervened between provider and patient, and patients themselves are more educated and demanding. Even in minor markets, it takes numerous *Yellow Pages* to list all the groups and providers a patient can choose from. Overcrowded media make it more difficult to gain consumer attention for your messages of medical excellence and patient-centered service.

The advent of health savings accounts (HSAs) brings a new challenge – individual consumers with discretionary money to spend are the antithesis of managed care. If payers have their way, patients will select physicians on the basis of tiered copayments. The net effect for medical practices: instead of signing contracts that bring "blocks" of patients to your practice, you'll be back to the equivalent of a fee-for-service environment, competing for patients one at a time.

How can your practice turn emerging market forces to its benefit? This section puts a new focus on traditional practice marketing and shows how top-notch service can give your practice a differential advantage over your competitors.

CHAPTER ONE

Building Market Share

"Marketing is knowing what your customers want
... making sure you deliver what they want ...
and letting them know you have it."

No one remembers who said it, but every marketing professional knows it's true.

Marketing begins by knowing the criteria patients use to select, stay loyal to, and refer others to your practice. With that knowledge, you align your work processes and physician/staff performance to satisfy customer expectations. And once you're sure that your practice can "deliver," you find the most effective ways to tell your target audiences that the place to find what they want is at your front door.

MARKETING PRIORITIES

Your service area is no longer a continually expanding pie, offering every practitioner a growing slice simply for being there. For a variety of reasons, medical marketing has become a "zero sum" game in which one practice prospers only at the expense of others.

In today's highly competitive environment, you have two marketing priorities: Protect the existing revenue base and generate new market share.

Priority #1 – *Protect the existing revenue base*

Consider the revenue you generated last year. As much as 90 percent of those dollars came from patients and/or referral sources who were in your computer on January 1; only a small portion of last year's profits was derived from new market share. So your first marketing priority is to protect what you have by ensuring that today's patient will return when future needs arise.

And the good news is that happy patients will be the major contributors to your second marketing priority.

Priority #2 – *Generate new market share*

Word-of-mouth referrals are the most effective, least expensive strategy for attracting new patients to your practice. Referrals constitute an implied "third-party endorsement," which carries great weight with people who are (a) seeking medical care for a newly diagnosed condition and/or (b) dissatisfied with their current medical care provider and looking for better service elsewhere.

Now that we've established what we're trying to accomplish with medical marketing, let's address the first element in the quote that began this chapter.

WHAT PATIENTS WANT

Service is the best strategy for protecting your existing revenue base and generating new patient volume.

That's a relatively recent phenomenon. Years ago, doctors talked about the importance of the "three As" – ability, availability, and affability. A 1980s medical management text talked about access, timely communication, and positive outcomes. In a 1993 focus group, a time-conscious patient said "I want the doctor to tell me what I have, how I got it, what I should do, and how long it will take to get better."

 SUCCESS SCENARIO

In March 2006, Mayo Clinic published the results of a study in which patients in several medical specialties were asked to describe the best and worst doctor visits they could remember. From the responses, the researchers distilled the specific behav-

iors that patients want from their doctors: confident, empa-
thetic, humane, personal, forthright, respectful and thorough.[1]

The MGMA-Sullivan/Luallin Patient Survey Program[SM] provides a more
data-driven way to prove the point that customer service is your best
practice marketing tool.[2] Exhibit 1.1 is based on our national multispecialty database which, as of this writing, contains more than 330,000
individual patient responses; it lists the survey questions that have the
highest correlation with patients' overall satisfaction (question F1 on the
survey form in Appendix A). Beta coefficients identify survey questions
that have the greatest effect on responses to the dependent variable – in
this case, question F1. Any question with a beta coefficient higher than
.500 is significantly correlated with overall satisfaction.

EXHIBIT 1.1
TYPICAL CORRELATION ANALYSIS
SURVEY QUESTIONS AFFECTING OVERALL SATISFACTION

SURVEY QUESTION	BETA COEFFICIENT
The courtesy of the person who took your call	.771
Helpfulness of the people who assisted with billing/insurance	.749
The doctor explaining things in a way you could understand	.746
Our ability to return your phone calls in a timely manner	.737
Your ability to obtain an appointment in reasonable time	.733
The friendliness of the receptionist	.726
The caring concern of our nurses/medical assistants	.705
The amount of time the doctor spent with you	.702
The doctor taking time to answer your questions	.701
The doctor clearly explaining your treatment options	.690

© 2006 MGMA-Sullivan/Luallin Patient Survey Program

Notice that the questions on the survey represent *service issues* – that is,
the score depends entirely or significantly on how your people perform,
as opposed to the quickness or smoothness of your processes for getting

the work done. For example, with "the courtesy of the person who took your call," there is a process (e.g., answering the call within three rings); however, our focus group findings are consistent with Mayo Clinic's conclusion that, when patients are dissatisfied, the speed of answering is less important than how the appointment secretary performs during the call.

The beta coefficients confirm the importance of service. As we noted earlier, this makes sense for another reason: patients cannot differentiate between providers on the basis of medical quality; they simply lack the technical knowledge to do so.

Think back to your last airline flight. When you boarded the plane, did you turn toward the cockpit and ask to see the pilot's license? Of course not. We all assume that pilots are fully qualified and know what they're doing. So we find our seats in the passenger section and get ready for the flight. Airlines know that they don't compete for your business on the basis of technical qualifications; their research says you want on-time departure and arrival, friendly flight attendants, a comfortable seat, and your bags arriving at the same airport that you do – these are "service" issues.

It's the same with medical professionals. Patients usually don't question the doctor's competence or ask about the medical assistant's training. Even the lowest-ranked graduate of medical school is still called "Doctor." And if we know nothing else, the lab coats and stethoscopes are enough to persuade us that we're in the hands of trained professionals.

Physicians and clinical teams are obsessively dedicated to medical quality, which for patients is a "given." When asked for their opinion of a doctor or clinic, they invariably talk about the service – how it feels to be your patient.

In the mid-1980s, the late Lewis Grizzard, then a columnist at the *Atlanta Constitution*, spoke to a convention of heart surgeons in Las Vegas. His subject dealt with the clearly evolving consumer desire for caring, responsive service. Halfway through his remarks, noticing that few physicians were paying attention, he put his notes aside and said, "Doctors, what I really came here to tell you is that you went to school for what you do while I'm asleep . . . but you make your money while I'm awake."

That's how health care consumers differentiate among doctors. Unless there's a strong negative associated with the practice – a widely publicized malpractice suit, for instance – they evaluate your practice on how you perform during telephone calls and the on-site encounter.

If we're agreed on the importance of service, let's turn to the second issue – ensuring that your practice can meet the service expectations of patients and their family members.

WHAT YOU CAN DO

The second step in marketing is making sure you deliver what customers want.

Medical groups have both strengths and weak-nesses; if yours is like most practices, you're happy with some of your survey scores and dis-mayed by others. As a good marketer, you want your entire team to maintain the higher scores and raise the lower ones.

> *Besides, service trumps process – that is, patients will overlook minor glitches in check-in, rooming, and so on as long as your providers and staff convey an atmosphere of welcome, friendliness, and caring concern.*

Some of the survey questions have to do with work processes – your sys-tems and procedures for patient intake and throughput. For example, one question asks about satisfaction with the waiting time in reception, while another question deals with your process for letting patients know about their test results.

We've all read the books on Continuous Quality Improvement (CQI), and we know the value of analyzing work processes, brainstorming pos-sible improvements, and implementing and testing solutions. Because the focus of this book is on service, we'll agree that making your patient-handling systems smooth and hassle-free is an essential part of increas-ing satisfaction and leave this subject to other authors.

Besides, *service trumps process* – that is, patients will overlook minor glitches in check-in, rooming, and so on as long as your providers and staff convey an atmosphere of welcome, friendliness, and caring concern. With this in mind, we'll restrict our focus to the performance aspects of delivering Star-Studded Service.

Managing for customer service

Years ago, when physicians and practice managers first recognized the importance of customer service, their initial approaches centered on staff performance. The assumption was that employees instinctively know how to be friendly and caring – after all, we're *people persons* – and all that's necessary is to remind staff members to treat patients as valued guests. Meetings about customer service were basically motivational pep talks; the trouble was, the effects were short-lived as employees returned to the daily grind of their jobs.

Managing for customer service is a matter of defining expectations, giving employees the skills and techniques needed to meet/exceed the expectations, holding them accountable for making patients feel valued and important, and rewarding top contributors. It requires a cohesive management system in which:

- Leadership is supportive and actively involved;

- Managers and supervisors continuously monitor performance levels, and react quickly when less-than-satisfactory behaviors are observed; and

- Providers and staff members know what's expected of them, have the skills to deliver it, and are supported when they do.

Chapters Four through Nine are devoted to a detailed explanation of the performance management concept.

MARKETING STRATEGIES

Once you're confident that your practice will meet the expectations of its customers, it's time to tell your world what you'll deliver when they come to you for care. You have many external vehicles for attracting new patients while reinforcing the loyalty of your existing patient base. You place display ads to announce the arrival of a new physician. Your newsletter touts a new practice site or service. You make contact with health and lifestyle writers at local papers and periodicals. Your Website helps patients schedule appointments or refill a prescription.

We'll leave the discussion of external marketing techniques to other authors and focus attention in this book on *service* – which, if we're to believe the beta coefficients presented earlier, is the most effective strategy for achieving your two marketing objectives.

BENEFITS OF HAVING A SERVICE CULTURE

You know that caring is part of the cure. But some of your associates – from the most senior physician to the receptionist you hired yesterday – may not share your view. They need to understand (and you're probably the best person to tell them!) that delivering top-level service benefits the practice as well as patients.

Greater productivity

Patient satisfaction provides a focal point for cooperation among physicians, clinical employees, and support staff to work together toward a common objective, and to accept new ideas in the interest of achieving it. It improves teamwork and cooperation both within and between departments. It gives people a reason to change.

Physicians will cooperate if you give them the chance. The doctors at Central Brooklyn Medical Group, much like physicians everywhere, gave the following responses to a recent survey:

EXHIBIT 1.2

**PHYSICIAN SURVEY –
CENTRAL BROOKLYN MEDICAL GROUP**

Would you change your practice patterns to achieve:	
	YES
. . . better medical outcomes	85.5%
. . . greater patient satisfaction	87.1%
. . . better staff morale	87.0%

Your Customer Service initiative can build on this willingness, and because employee attitudes are largely a reflection of leadership attitudes, the physicians' enthusiasm is bound to filter down throughout the practice. We all know that staff members perform according to their perceptions of how the doctors feel about patient satisfaction. When we're asked to improve the performance of employees who are drifting through their workday, our first task is to assess what messages the doctors are sending, by word or action, to let staff members know how to treat patients.

SUCCESS SCENARIO

If you ask them, your physicians will probably say that service is important and patient satisfaction should be a top priority. You can test their resolve by asking the following question at an upcoming partner meeting: "Suppose that I'm on your clinical staff and have to choose between making you happy or making a patient happy ... which do you want me to choose?" Their answers will tell you what they really believe about patient satisfaction.

Better medical outcomes

Beginning with clinical studies in the 1980s, the connection between "positive effect" and medical outcomes has been well established. Patients who see their doctor or nurse as caring and concerned are more likely to comply with the treatment plan – taking all the medication, showing up for follow-on visits, and sticking to diet and exercise regimens – with the predictable result that their medical outcomes are better than for those patients who are dissatisfied with their providers.

Stronger risk management

Similarly, insurers point to good doctor-patient relationships as a major factor in preventing malpractice claims. According to various industry studies, nearly 70 percent of lawsuits against doctors result from either lack of informed consent ("I didn't know that would happen!") or perceptions that the provider was evasive, distant, rushed, or even arrogant and uncaring.

Reduced turnover

In every industry, employees who feel that they are appreciated by their customers tend to enjoy their jobs more and, as a consequence, are less likely to look for another place of employment when the going gets rough. Further, there's an *esprit de corps* that comes from knowing that one is part of a "sharp outfit" with satisfied customers and talented colleagues who like and respect each other. The payoff is pride in one's organization, personal career satisfaction, and sustained enthusiasm for tackling the tough tasks that accompany any worthwhile job.

Our next chapter explores the realities of practice building in a competitive marketplace. We'll explore the implications of competing for loyalty and referrals in a service area where customer demands are evolving and the most successful practices will be those that recognize and adjust to changing market priorities.

CHAPTER TWO

Factors Affecting Patient Satisfaction

"Give the lady what she wants."

MARSHALL FIELD

In earlier times – an era when Henry Ford would promise a car "in any color, as long as it's black" – Marshall Field built a retailing empire in the Midwest by recognizing that consumers, not suppliers, would eventually have the final say in determining which companies would succeed, and which would likely not.

Throughout the 20th century, medical groups learned the same lesson. Decades of focusing almost exclusively on medical excellence – physicians actually talked about "patient loyalty" as if medicine were uniquely exempt from market forces – were replaced by a grudging admission that patients, not providers, would assert their preferences for caring along with curing.

Today it's all different.

 SUCCESS SCENARIO

"At SHARP Rees-Stealy Medical Group we have a rule from which no one is exempt," says Dr. Donald Balfour, Chief Executive Officer. "Every encounter with an external or internal customer is concluded with the phrase 'Is there anything else I can do for you?'

"At first, our doctors and employees resisted the idea, thinking that the statement would sound false, or would take too much time, or might add needlessly to an already crowded workday. But now it's become a way of life, and we can see how positively our patients have reacted to our willingness to make an extra effort for them."

WHO ARE YOUR CUSTOMERS?

Patients come in all shapes and sizes; they have different needs and wants.[3]

Seniors – the Silent Generation

Born before 1945, seniors come from a heritage of duty, honor, and dedication to country. They understand the meaning of sacrifice, and their "we first" attitudes indicate respect for group conformity – blending in and working patiently toward goals were the values that brought them through hard times to prosperity. They know that "doing a good job" is important and they believe that age confers a seniority that entitles them to special consideration.

Meeting seniors' service expectations means showing courtesy and respect; addressing them by their last names (until you sense that more familiarity is appropriate); greeting them with a smile and a pleasant welcome; speaking distinctly, with a willingness to repeat statements if it appears they don't understand; patience when they get upset or need special attention; keeping them informed of their status in reception and the exam room; and saying a friendly good-bye.

Baby Boomers

Born between 1945 and 1964, Baby Boomers measure themselves by their work ethic; they throw themselves into their jobs (this is the generation that coined the term "workaholic"). They're proud of their success, as defined by job accomplishments, and show it in ways others can see. They are optimistic and enjoy personal development, and they know the song lyrics "We are the world, we are the children."

Meeting Boomers' service expectations means respecting their accomplishments in the form of quick responses, politeness, and attention to their desire for recognition; using "sir" and "ma'am," and compliment-ing them on their appearance; having interesting and topical reading materials in lobby and exam room; and demonstrating the courtesy they believe they've earned by their achievements.

Generation X

Born between 1965 and 1980, Gen X-ers learned at an early age to ques-tion authority. They've lost faith in institutions and instead have invested their trust and loyalty in peers. They do not see relationships as life-long obligations and are willing to switch loyalties for their own rea-sons. They're not interested in sacrificing to achieve success. Because they were raised as their parents' "friends," they resist being instructed by oth-ers and adopt a "prove it to me" attitude when vendors make claims about service and superiority.

Meeting Gen X-ers' service expectations means delivering on your prom-ises quickly and efficiently; training doctors and staff in techniques that promote individual relationships; converting your "we care about you" message into extra-step efforts that Gen X-ers can see; finding ways to thank them for their business ("Is there anything else I can do for you?"); and, instead of dictating to them, giving them choices that make them feel like partners in their health care ("Would you prefer a morning sur-gery, or is the afternoon better for you?").

Millennials

Born after 1980, Millennials are optimistic and busy with their lives. They value membership in a group as long as it's *their* group. Because they've been taught to question everything, they don't believe advertising claims or the "we care" message in your new patient brochure. They measure their own job success by whether they get the work done on time, not by how many hours they work each week. They have difficulty focusing on "non-stimulating stuff," and they aren't comfortable thinking too far into the future, whether at the burger palace or the doctor's office.

Meeting Millennials' service expectations means making the most of their time (e.g., leaving "advance access" slots for same-day work-ins); teaching doctors and employees to frame their explanations in clear, con-cise, and straightforward messages; remembering birthdays, babies' names, and other personal information that recognizes their individuality; respecting their comfort with technology by making the decision to employ Web communications for appointment self-scheduling, prescription refills, and even two-way interchange with professional staff.

(Of course, there's plenty of overlap in the patient-pleasing techniques mentioned in the preceding paragraphs – for example, seniors appreciate same-day access just like Millennials do. The point is that savvy marketers know that patient expectations differ by age group, and they teach their colleagues to recognize and respond to these differences.)

THE VALUE EQUATION

"I worked all day to earn his fee," a patient once told a practice manager, "but the doctor spent less than ten minutes with me!"

From studies begun two decades ago, medical researchers, who knew that providers had to respond to patients' power of choice — realized that *time* is among the most important considerations for coping with an increasingly chaotic world. In fact, time is one of the most important elements of "cost" in the following equation:

$$\frac{\text{MEDICAL OUTCOME} + \text{SERVICE}}{\text{COST}} = \text{VALUE}$$

Mathematically inclined readers will like this equation. It suggests that patients judge their medical experience in terms of outcome ("did I get the results I expected?") and service ("how did it feel to be your patient?"), vs. cost ("how easy or difficult was my experience?"). Because "medical outcome" is a given – patients assume that the professionals they encounter are qualified and that following their advice will likely better their condition – the only ways you can increase patients' perception of "value" is either to increase the "service" or decrease the "cost."

Time is a "cost" to patients, and service industries recognize this fact. In a single generation we've gone from "Please wait until we're ready for you" to ATMs, fast food, and online banking. Medicine knows this, too – witness the popularity of express clinics, same-day appointments, and refilling prescriptions on the practice Website.

That's one reason why reducing the time spent waiting in your reception area and exam room is a critical priority – in fact, survey questions relating to waiting time often receive the lowest scores. Visiting the doctor's office is only one slice of the patient's life, and patients constantly compare the time they spend at your practice with the time they spend accessing other services.

You're in competition with the time spent at a fast-food restaurant – most people know that, if there are six or more cars in the drive-thru lane at McDonald's, it's faster to park and go inside. You're being compared with the local bank, where customers avoid the inside lines by using the ATM or conducting their business online. And the next patient who enters your practice has just come from a dry cleaner that features one-hour Martinizing.

 SUCCESS SCENARIO

Minute Clinic is a Minneapolis-based chain that advertises "You're sick – we're quick." Located in high-traffic retail centers, especially near pharmacies, they emphasize convenience at a reasonable cost (between $49 and $59 for a visit) by using mid-level providers and streamlining the system for processing common illnesses that are nonurgent, but still important to patients, like bronchitis, bladder or ear infections, and immunizations. Minute Clinic, with centers in nine states, opened more than 30 new clinics in less than two months (*HealthLeaders*, January 2006).

"Cost" is also measured in "hassle." Patients – particularly younger ones – resent standing in line at check-in, not knowing when the doctor will enter the exam room, waiting for a telephone call-back, the interval between a test and receiving test results, and every other aspect of accessing the health care system.

The patient's perception of time is less a function of actual minutes than about what happens during the wait. In Appendix H, we'll suggest strategies for generating higher survey scores even if you can't reduce waiting times.

The beta coefficients on page 7 argue strongly for increasing service as your most effective strategy for ensuring patient loyalty (protecting the existing revenue) and referrals (generating tomorrow's market share).

SUCCESS SCENARIO

You're not alone in seeking information about your patients' satisfaction; others are watching, too. The following questions are part of the CAHPS "Clinician and Group Survey," which has been in field tests since 2004, and contains questions such as these from the September 2005 version of the survey:[4]

- In the last 12 months, when you called this doctor's office during regular office hours, how often did you get an answer to your medical question that same day?

- In the last 12 months, how often did your visits to this doctor's office start *within 15 minutes* of your appointment?

- In the last 12 months, how often did this doctor explain things in a way that was easy to understand?

- In the last 12 months, how often did this doctor listen carefully to you?

- In the last 12 months, how often did this doctor give you easy to understand instructions about taking care of these health problems or concerns?

- In the last 12 months, how often did this doctor show respect for what you had to say?

- In the last 12 months, how often did this doctor spend enough time with you?

- In the last 12 months, how often were clerks and receptionists at this doctor's office as helpful as you thought they should be?

- In the last 12 months, how often did clerks and receptionists at this doctor's office treat you with courtesy and respect?

So now we have the rationale for service. Let's raise the stakes by adding one other factor – in competing for patient volume, *you're chasing a moving target!* Each year, mean scores in the MGMA-Sullivan/Luallin national patient survey database are rising.

Exhibit 2.1 shows that after a slight softening in 2002, the influence of "pay for performance" and other market forces have put new impetus into practice marketing plans. (Although the database figures are for primary care practices, the same trend applies to specialist practices in competitive markets.)

EXHIBIT 2.1

**AVERAGE MEAN SCORES 2000–2006
PRIMARY CARE PRACTICES
(Scale 1–5)**

	2000	2002	2004	2006
Access	4.04	4.02	4.09	4.11
Staff performance	4.41	4.36	4.38	4.39
Communication	4.09	4.06	4.10	4.12
Physician performance	4.42	4.45	4.46	4.48
Overall satisfaction	4.42	4.39	4.40	4.41

©2006 MGMA-Sullivan/Luallin Patient Survey Program

The conclusion is clear: If your patient survey scores are "flat" from year to year, you're really falling behind!

So why are some practices forging ahead while others have trouble keeping up with the pace? In Part Two, we'll describe the six-step process that small and large groups are using to stay ahead of their competitors. Before proceeding, though, there's one final issue to cover – how to build the team that will deliver the service levels that build patient loyalty and market share.

Our next chapter treats the subject of finding, recruiting, hiring, and building the team that will deliver on your promise of stellar customer service.

CHAPTER THREE

Building the Service Team

"Our chief want in life is somebody who will
make us do what we can."

RALPH WALDO EMERSON

If you were the manager of a manufacturing assembly line, you wouldn't care if your employees were friendly or courteous to customers, for the simple reason that your customers would never see them! Customers make purchases on the basis of whether the product appeals to them, not whether they like the people who made it.

It's different in a medical clinic. Your people *are* the product, and customer satisfaction depends as much on people skills as on the outcome of the treatment – in fact, as we've demonstrated earlier, perceptions of service (not medical quality) are the determining factors in building patient loyalty and referrals.

In a group practice, no one gets the job done alone. Everyone needs the help of co-workers and people in support departments. Over the years, we've done research in this area through employee surveys and focus groups, and the most common feeling we've heard is that "we cooperate pretty well within our department, but there's not much teamwork *between* departments."

In staff seminars, we ask nurses, receptionists, technicians, and employees in the business office why they work in the medical profession, and the answer is always the same – "I wanted to help people." (Those who study neurolinguistics have noted that when employees answer this question, they typically use the past tense ("I wanted to . . ."); they wonder if enthusiasm for working in a service industry gradually erodes the noble ambitions that accompanied the job application.)

SUCCESS SCENARIO

Joyce Curtiss manages the call centers of Beaver Medical Group (Calif.), which typically handles more than 6,000 phone requests every day. Even with more than 50 employees, the department was understaffed for the workload, and the strain of coping with heavy workloads was reflected in patient reactions to how employees "came across" while making appointments for them – their mean score for the item "The courtesy of the person who took your call" was 4.27 (1-5 scale), ranking them at the 43rd percentile of the multi-specialty database.

"We're the call center for more than 140 doctors practicing in 12 facilities," Joyce says, "and the main switchboard for incoming calls. We also maintain the walk-up appointment desks in our main clinic. It's a big department where most people see each other only at periodic meetings.

"We needed a strategy that would build teamwork while improving customer service," Joyce adds. "We chose baseball because winning teams make the World Series by playing well together and we expected that generating internal goodwill would show in the way we treat our customers.

"Our 'spring training' was conducted by the former president of our group, who came back to get the program started. He spoke about the important part we play in customer service and threw out the first ball. I thanked him with a bag of peanuts, and we both hawked 'Peanuts ... red-hot peanuts' while tossing bags into the group. Everyone was inspired and ready to go!

"We divided our large workforce into teams based on location and mission and appointed captains who would serve as cheerleaders and motivators. The rules were based on doing a good job. Teams advanced around the bases by making hits and home runs linked to following clinic and department rules; strikes and outs were linked to scheduling errors and not following the rules. When a team struck out, all other teams advanced one base. And we kept highly visible poster-boards to let everyone keep track of their scores.

"The highest-scoring team enjoyed a pizza party at the end of April – 60 days after we had reviewed the baseline survey report. Along the way, for every home run we distributed 'star' awards redeemable for prizes. We never lost the enthusiasm."

The bottom line: a follow-on patient survey conducted in April 2006 showed a mean score of 4.32 for the question "The courtesy of the person who took your call" – a statistically significant improvement of 9.6 percentile points compared with the previous survey.

So here's a question for you: Two candidates have applied for an opening in your billing department, where employees are often on the telephone answering patients' questions. One has lots of billing experience and knows the procedures, but has few people skills; the other is loaded with people skills, but has little experience in billing systems. Whom would you hire?

No contest, right? You'd hire the applicant with people instincts, and so would we. Any willing person can learn the procedural parts of a job (and besides, before you meet a candidate, you already know from the application that they have the requisite job experience).

In selecting the members of your team, you're looking for two additional attributes – the instincts that will produce service-centered performance in even the toughest situations and the team thinking that will inspire cooperation even when requests from other employees come at the worst possible moment.

BUILDING YOUR TEAM

So let's talk about how you'll build your team of customer-sensitive professionals – and what it will take to keep them that way.

Interview for service instincts

The applicant is prepared. She arrives on time, properly dressed and groomed, and smiles as she waits for your first question. She looks relaxed.

You, on the other hand, are desperate. It's been several weeks since the job opening was posted, and you've been juggling staff and personally covering for the absence of a full-time employee in this position. In the interim, you've neglected your own work and your in-box is full of unattended stuff. You need to hire someone, and fast; moreover, a quick review of the application form shows that she has the required certification and even a few years working in another clinic.

It looks like a slam-dunk hire, but you're holding back until another, equally important issue is resolved to your satisfaction. Does she understand the importance of patient satisfaction? How will she react in a demanding situation? What will she do if a patient complains or an employee from another department needs a favor? Will she be a good "fit" with the other members of your team?

Applicants are well rehearsed, and they're expecting trick questions like, "What's your greatest weakness?" They're ready with a good answer to that one, such as "My greatest weakness is that I get terribly frustrated when I can't accomplish everything I want to achieve." So we always ask, "And what's your second-greatest weakness?" People rarely prepare for that question, but the answer tells us what's in the applicant's heart.

Regardless of the technical qualifications, knowing what's in the heart of an applicant is the best way to predict the performance you'll get in the busy environment of ringing phones, over-booked schedules, and continual interruptions. The key is to ask open-ended questions (not the yes/no kind) that offer clues to how a person really feels about the service s/he will be expected to deliver.

SUCCESS SCENARIO

Melanie Saunders is Human Resource Director for Arizona Medical Group, a multi-specialty practice with more than 80 providers and five practice facilities. "We believe in developing a full profile of every applicant before extending a job offer," she says, "because our intent is to hire service-centered people who will put our patients ahead of other concerns, even when the going gets rough. We've developed a list of interview questions that accomplish our objective while conforming to regulatory standards for respecting confidentiality, and all of our supervisors use it when meeting a job applicant."

Here is Melanie's list of recommended interview questions:

1. What are three positive things that your last boss would say about you?

2. Why did you leave your last job?

3. What was your most significant accomplishment in your last job?

4. Give an example of a stressful work situation and how you handled it.

5. What is a work-related weakness you feel you could improve upon and how would you go about seeking improvement?

6. How would you handle conflict with a co-worker?

7. Explain what you think a typical day is like in the position you are applying for? (REFER TO THE JOB DESCRIPTION)

8. How would you describe yourself in terms of your ability to work in a team?

9. Are you able to manage multiple high-priority jobs? How would you prioritize those jobs?

10. What can you do for us that others can't?

Arizona Medical Group's approach to interviewing allows each manager to distinguish between equally qualified candidates on the basis of service instincts. New hires who already understand the value of customer satisfaction don't have to be taught how to relate to patients and their family members. (In fact, some experts would argue that service instincts can't be taught – we can define behaviors and insist that patient-contact employees use them, but patients are experts at spotting someone who's going through the motions simply because they have to.)

Communicate your expectations

People need to know what you stand for; they also need to know what you *won't* stand for. The next step in building a service team is to ensure that everyone knows what standards they must meet as a condition of employment, and how serious you are about enforcing them.

"Ultimately the responsibility for setting performance standards falls on the immediate supervisor," according to Susan Graham, Human Resources Director of Buenaventura Medical Group (Ventura, Calif.). "You can hire professionals to train employees in the skills needed to meet service standards, but employees know they're not accountable to trainers. That's why we reinforce our staff training seminars with an immediate structure for first-line supervisors to let their people know that the standards are not mere suggestions – they represent benchmarks for holding ourselves accountable for meeting and exceeding service standards."

Susan is among the HR executives who help managers and supervisors by providing a formal structure for conveying the service message. She advises a series of "hallway huddles" – 15 to 20 minutes either before the morning schedule or during a catered lunch hour – in which supervisors follow an agenda similar to the following:

EXHIBIT 3.1

STEP	ACTIVITY	REMARKS
1	Choose a protocol	
2	Schedule meeting	Set date/time; choose a place away from the office bustle
3	Announce meeting	Send the agenda to all employees
4	Facilitate meeting	Review the service protocol
		Discuss how the protocols apply to their jobs
		Ask what could prevent meeting the protocols
5	Post-meeting	Monitor and give feedback as needed

At Buenaventura Medical Group, each supervisor was required to confirm that the meetings were held and to develop a personal action plan describing their individual strategies for holding people accountable for meeting/exceeding the standards. (In Chapter Six we'll discuss service protocols in greater detail and provide examples that you can attach to job descriptions and use in day-to-day coaching of your employees.)

Keep your people informed

Feedback is the breakfast of champions. In the context of team building, information is more important than you might think. A characteristic of effective teams is that the members are always measuring themselves – they want to know what's going on and how they're doing.

Think back to high school. Remember how it felt to be part of the "in crowd" – or not? For members of the "in crowd," there was a security in knowing they *belonged*, and they translated that security into what we called "school spirit." Those on the outside, knowing they weren't likely to penetrate the inner circle, had a very different view of things – they were more likely to be loners, initially resentful of their outsider status and eventually negative about the organization. For them, school spirit was less important.

It's the same with employees in a medical practice. When you keep people "in on things," they feel more like team members and naturally identify with the success of the practice. They understand what you're trying to accomplish and are more willing to support your strategies. (This is as true for physicians as for staff members.)

Employee newsletters – however informal – are effective team-building vehicles. For practices with intranet capability, frequent messages keep everyone "in on things." Periodic hallway huddles provide opportunities for sharing information about plans and progress.

Thank people for their efforts

From reviewing employee survey results (see Chapter Four), it's easy to identify employees who feel like team members, and those who don't. Among the clues are comments about recognition – as you might imagine, people want a work environment in which their efforts are recognized and rewarded.

SUCCESS SCENARIO

Dr. Abe Levy is Medical Director and Chief Quality Officer of Mount Kisco Medical Group (Mount Kisco, N.Y.), where the leadership team believes solidly in recognizing the extra-step efforts of employees.

"One of the turning points for us was adding the focus of becoming an 'employer of choice' where people are happy to come to work," Dr. Levy says. "This is not a matter of salary alone; while salaries must be fair and competitive in the marketplace, employees need more than money."

Dr. Levy points to several efforts developed by the leadership team:

1. An ice cream truck pulls up to the office every other Friday from May to September, and employees are treated to whatever item they want, just by showing the group ID card. During winter months, cider and doughnuts are provided free of charge.

2. An annual employee appreciation day features a picnic lunch, served by the physicians and practice executives, where years of service are honored, as well as retiring employees.

3. The summer employee picnic includes all members of the practice team and their family members. Six months later, the clinic hosts a festive holiday party in formal dress, with open bar, sit-down dinner, and a Viennese dessert table.

4. Every employee receives a holiday bonus toward year-end, and when the year has been exceptionally successful, an additional "surprise" bonus is personally delivered to each employee's work station by Dr. Scott Hayworth, President and CEO of Mount Kisco Medical Group.

"Accompanying each of these activities is an e-mail to all team members explaining that the thank-you is due to their wonderful efforts to promote patient satisfaction," adds Dr. Levy.

"We say it in different ways, but the message is always the same – Mount Kisco physicians are grateful for the superb customer service our employees provide our patients."

Please notice that in this discussion of building the service team, we've stayed away from traditional approaches of team building. That's because we believe your focus is better spent on how the team performs rather than how its members feel about each other. You'll find plenty of information about team building in other manuals – role plays and team exercises, discussion topics and self-assessment tools – we're all for that.

Clearly, the focus in this chapter is on the behaviors that contribute to patient loyalty and referrals – hiring the right people, defining what's expected, and making sure they know what they'll be held accountable for.

This concludes Part One. Now we're ready to present a proven strategy that you can use – regardless of your practice size, specialty, or geographic region – to protect your existing revenue base and build new patient volume.

PART TWO

SIX STEPS TO SERVICE EXCELLENCE

"To love what you do and feel that it matters –
how could anything be more fun?"

KATHARINE GRAHAM

WHAT SEPARATES SERVICE SUPERSTARS FROM THE "WANNABES?"

Since the 1980s, when "marketing" first entered the lexicon of medical group leaders, we've known that service is an integral part of health care delivery. But how do you create and maintain a service culture? And how do you keep it going once you start?

The following chapters describe a proven approach to lifting customer service through a formal Customer Service Initiative. (Please note that we use the word "initiative" instead of "program" to describe your patient satisfaction strategy – "program" connotes a short-term effort with discrete start and end points; if customer service is your long-term strategy for ensuring the health of your business, the effort needs to be elevated above the typical "program of the month.")

The Customer Service Initiative has six steps – in more than two decades of consulting with small and large clients, we've found each step is an essential part of involving your physicians and employees in a sustained effort that outlives the initial enthusiasm of most "programs." The aim is to install patient-centered performance as a continuous way of doing business at your practice. The strategy mirrors the management system you and your physicians already use to guarantee the highest quality of medical care.

The six steps also make business sense – they represent the approach used by group practices that achieve their objectives for revenue and market share, and qualify highest for the "pay for performance" incentives currently offered by health plans in a growing number of U.S. markets.

Step One (Chapter Four) describes the *baseline service assessment* that gives you a true profile of your service strengths and weaknesses and forms a foundation for the improvement activities that will follow.

Step Two (Chapter Five) introduces a new way to involve your physicians and staff in *building an action plan*, using a relatively new technique developed by reliability engineers in several U.S. industries and successfully adapted by health care organizations.

Step Three (Chapter Six) discusses the *service protocols* that enable physicians and staff to meet and exceed patients' service expectations – by the time you administer your next survey— while lifting insider morale.

Step Four (Chapter Seven) describes how to convey the protocols to your physicians, supervisors, and employees through lively and interactive *customer service seminars* tailored to the unique "science + service" atmosphere of group practice.

Step Five (Chapter Eight) will explain how to establish relevant *tracking systems* for letting your team know how they're doing, and holding people accountable for providing patient-centered service.

Finally, **Step Six** (Chapter Nine) contains recommendations for high-probability *momentum strategies* to ensure that the gains you make continue over the long term and that service excellence becomes part of your organization's culture.

CHAPTER FOUR

Step One:
Conducting a Baseline Service Assessment

"Measure a thousand times . . . cut once."

CHINESE PROVERB

The first step toward knowing where to go is to be sure of where you are.

A baseline service assessment examines how well you're serving your external and internal customers, including (but not limited to):

- A patient survey conducted at regular intervals and designed to provide relevant feedback from the patients' perspective;

- Mystery patient assessments, in which experienced professionals probe beyond the survey data to evaluate the specific performance dimensions that affect patient satisfaction;

- Key-person interviews to obtain input from the physicians and employees who work directly with patients and have the best ideas on how to improve service levels; and

- Related performance indicators that affect patient satisfaction, including staff turnover rates, requests for records transfer, trends in referrals from other physicians, anecdotal patient complaints, malpractice claims, and other data that measure the service strengths and weaknesses of your practice.

PATIENT SATISFACTION SURVEY

Because your business depends on patient loyalty and word-of-mouth referrals, patients are your best source of information about what works well and what needs to be improved. A patient survey is the best tool for asking them what they think of your practice.

Patient surveys used to be optional; if you wanted to know what patients were thinking about your practice and your people, a survey was a good way to find out. Sometimes, owing to human nature, the surveys were "whitewash jobs" designed to produce high marks so as not to offend physicians and employees.

That was then. Today, in our competitive marketplace, knowing where your practice stands with patients and caregivers is imperative, and managers who "fudge" the findings are underserving the practice.

A poorly designed survey shortchanges patients, too, because unrealistic data may not produce the improvements that would benefit them. That's why much study has gone into how surveys are constructed, how best to distribute them, what kind of reports are most helpful to practice leaders and managers, and how survey data can help you set priorities for improving the work processes and physician/staff service performance that affect patient satisfaction and referrals.

SURVEY DESIGN AND LAYOUT

Surveys are not perfect instruments. They are based on perceptions, which makes it difficult, even impossible, to set quantified norms for measuring performance.

(The inability to set quantified criteria is illustrated by one of the questions listed in the Success Scenario on page 20. The "Clinician and Group Survey" instrument asks, "In the last 12 months, how often did your visits to this doctor's office start *within 15 minutes* of your appointment?" Aiming for a quantifiable response does not take into account the inherent variability of patient expectations – one person can be dissatisfied with a 10-minute wait, while another may be content to sit for 30 minutes or longer in the reception area. If your purpose is to measure satisfaction, you're less interested in the length of the wait than in whether the patient was satisfied with the waiting time.)

So what should your patient survey look like? The questions are arranged to follow the patient's experience during the encounter as closely as possible, from making an appointment to checking out after the visit. Examine Appendix A on pages 111 and 112 and review the survey questions before reading the rest of this chapter.

—⸺⸺—

Okay, that was easy. Did you notice that the questions are stated as briefly and clearly as possible? That's to ensure *face validity* – that is, the respondent understands what the question is about and gives an answer related to the performance dimension being rated; and *content validity* – that is, the questions are grouped together in a manner reflecting what actually happens during the encounter. In the MGMA-Sullivan/Luallin survey (Appendix A) the questions are divided into five sections:

- Access (making appointments, check-in, and waiting times);
- Staff performance (reception, clinical staff, business office, and technical staff);
- Communication (information materials, test results, and other issues);
- Physician performance (exam room encounter); and
- Facility (comfort, cleanliness, parking, and signage).

Following the specific, visit-related issues are four general questions that compose a kind of final report card:

- Overall satisfaction with the practice;
- Overall satisfaction with the quality of medical care;
- Overall satisfaction with one's personal physician or nurse;
- Willingness to recommend the practice to family members and friends.

The survey fits on two sides of a single sheet of paper, which can increase the response rate without producing *survey fatigue* (the tendency of respondents to quit part way because they're tired of answering the questions). The form is anonymous and confidential, although many patients will add their name and phone number, particularly if they want to be contacted to discuss an issue of importance to them.

The rating scale is called a five-point Likert scale.[5] The descriptors conform to the layout of many health plan surveys, with choices ranging from "excellent" to "poor."

SURVEY DISTRIBUTION METHODS

You can distribute the survey either in the office or by mail.

Office distribution involves receptionists who ask patients to complete the survey either before leaving the office (depositing the survey in a collection box), or when they return home (using a stamped reply envelope). Typical response rates are between 30 to 40 percent, although some practices do better; the difference depends on how the receptionist offers the survey and emphasizes its importance to the practice's efforts to meet patients' expectations for comfortable, hassle-free services.

Mail distribution requires an accurate data file of patient names and addresses. Response rates are typically lower than for in-office surveys (20 to 25 percent, with some exceptions) and the collection period tends to be longer, typically five to six weeks.

Many physicians prefer mail surveys for the protection they offer against manipulation by practice insiders, especially when incentive bonuses depend on the scores. At the same time, mail surveys are about 70 percent more expensive, owing to .the costs of list management, mailing services, and outbound and reply postage.

WHAT'S NOT GOOD ABOUT TELEPHONE SURVEYS

Telephone surveys can present several issues. First, telephone surveys can often be the most expensive method, but proponents claim a better response rate (some say as high as 85 percent) and that interviewers can probe beyond the basic responses for more detailed and reliable information. In fact, the reverse is true for several reasons:

- Phone interviews require four to five computerized "dial attempts" to complete a single interview; using this ratio of attempts to completions, the response rate for phone surveys is well below that of office or mail distribution.

- Phone interviews can produce *acquiescence bias* – the tendency of respondents to give socially acceptable answers regardless of the content of the question (often to please the interviewer).

- Because of the relatively rapid question/answer interaction, patients are more likely to give similar answers to a series of questions (*central tendency*), resulting in less variation and less discrimination between survey issues.

- Because respondents are unable to visualize the rating scales, their focus is split between answering the questions and remembering the range of possible choices.

- The negative tone of interviewers probing for dissatisfaction can produce a more negative set of responses.

- Consumers are often antagonized by attempts to reach them during dinnertime or evening hours (the best time to find patients at home).

The anonymity afforded by self-administered paper surveys and the ability of respondents to answer at their own pace make written-response surveys more likely to produce data you can use. Further, anonymity encourages responses on sensitive issues and intimate details that many respondents are reluctant to discuss with telephone interviewers.

SAMPLE SIZE AND VALIDITY

Surveying every patient in your database would be prohibitively expensive. The population is too large to attempt to survey all of your patients. A small but carefully chosen *sample* can be used to represent all the patients who come to your practice for their medical care. The sample needs to reflect the characteristics of the population from which it is drawn.

You can derive valid information from a portion of your entire patient population as long as the sample you choose is *representative* – that is, the answers you get from the sample will be as close as possible to what all your patients would say, if you could ask them.

However, sampling has rules. In satisfaction research, the question is, to what extent can the sample in your report be projected across a physician's entire patient population? This question is often unanswerable because we can't know everything about every variable in the total population – age, gender, and so on. That's why "there is no such thing as a representative, unbiased, fair, or otherwise acceptable sample" (Stuart, 1968).

A key to valid sampling is to select a "random" number of patients for the survey. "Random" implies that every person in your patient population has an equal chance of being selected for the survey. In a mailed survey, you can approximate a random sample by asking the computer to select every third patient, or every patient seen on Monday, or by several other criteria. For in-office distribution, you can come close to a random sample by choosing a starting point from which every patient is offered a chance to take the survey, until all surveys have been distributed. The assumption is that patients randomize themselves by making an appointment with the doctor during the distribution period.

So let's accept that the sample is as "random" as we can make it. The next question is, how many surveys do you need to make reasonable statements about how a physician is viewed by his/her patients? A sample size generally agreed on among statisticians (and medical directors) is 30 qualified responses.[6]

The "30 or more" criterion is also nonscientific. It represents a compromise between the money you can afford to spend and the statistical validity that will persuade your colleagues to accept the results of sampling only a portion of your patient base.

Sample size computations measure only statistical sampling errors; many other sources of error can influence the accuracy and reliability of the survey findings – coverage errors, nonresponse errors, respondent mistakes, questionnaire defects, and administrative errors. Exhibit 4.1 shows that the sampling error associated with a population of 30 completed surveys is about ±14.0 percent.

There are no guarantees regarding how many patients will complete your survey. Because over-the-counter surveys usually produce response rates of 30 to 40 percent, we recommend a distribution of 100 surveys per physician. If you're looking for a summary report for a practice site, a return of 200 completed surveys would have a sampling error of about ±6.0 percent – which, for a marketing study, is sufficient for identifying where the site excels, and where it needs to improve.

But what if a physician receives fewer than 30 responses? Can you still say something relevant about the doctor's performance if the sample size is, say 20 surveys? Sure you can – just not with the same confidence as if

EXHIBIT 4.1

SAMPLING ERROR FOR PATIENT SURVEYS

SAMPLE SIZE	SAMPLING ERROR (±)
25	16.0%
50	11.2%
75	9.1%
100	7.8%
150	6.4%
250	5.0%
500	3.5%
750	2.9%
1,000	2.5%
1,500	2.0%

Weeks, J.L. et al., 1996

the sample size were larger. Conclusions drawn from 20 surveys are valid – just not as valid as conclusions drawn from a larger sample. (Please note that these are rough rule-of-thumb numbers – the actual formula for determining sampling error is complex and involves several independent variables.)

A final thought about sample sizes: Because there's no way to eliminate sampling errors completely, what matters most is that all physicians are treated the same – that is, everyone uses the same survey form, the survey is conducted during the same period, and it has the same distribution methodology. If any error in the process is constant across your entire physician population or across all the practices in the benchmarking database, the comparisons are valid even if the scores are less than exact.

REPORTING

Survey reports should be designed with the user's need in mind; the key is to ask yourself, at the start of the project, what you intend to do with the data you receive. Although there are many interesting conclusions that can be drawn from analyzing the data, the primary purposes of the report are to enable practice leaders (a) to identify "what works and what doesn't" in terms of meeting or exceeding patients' expectations for service, and (b) to set priorities for improvement.

Physicians and practice managers tell us they want survey reports that are easy to read without the need for an interpretation guide. Appendix B contains a sample survey report, showing the percentage responses to each question from "excellent" to "poor." Please take a moment to review the report in Appendix B on pages 113–117.

Welcome back. Let's review what you saw in the sample report. Here's the analysis we apply when using survey data to design Customer Service initiatives.

In Section One, the percentage response to each survey question tells us the following:

- "Excellent" and "Very Good" responses represent your friends and fans. These respondents are loyal to your practice and would probably resist a competitor's moves to take them away from you. Their satisfaction also means that they're saying good things about you to their families and friends. (Some practices favor using only the "Excellent" percentages, believing that anything lower signifies less-than-loyal patients.)

- "Fair" and "Poor" responses signify the opposite. These patients are not loyal and would probably change to another doctor or practice if they suspect that they might receive better service elsewhere. Their dissatisfaction means that they're not saying good things about you.

  (A study by Humana in the 1980s indicated that satisfied patients are likely to tell 2 to 3 others about you, whereas dissatisfied patients will probably tell 11 to 13 others why they don't like you. Other studies put the negative potential even higher. Expressed in marketing terms, the upside potential of satisfying your patients is far outweighed by the downside potential of antagonizing them.)

- The column about which we can speak with the least confidence is represented by the "Good" responses. As the midpoint of the scale, the "Good" category can be seen as representing patients who are essentially neutral about your practice. ("Nothing happened that delighted me, but you didn't antagonize me, either.") These patients are like the "undecideds" in an election year – they can stay with you or leave, depending on a wide variety of factors.

The bottom line is that the total of "Excellent" and "Very Good" responses indicates your marketing strength; if you want to approximate your potential for losing patients, simply add the percentages in the "Good to Poor" columns.

Please look again at Appendix B – particularly the percentage scores for Question F1 on page 117 ("Your overall satisfaction with our practice"). Adding "good," "fair," and "poor" scores shows that 13.5 percent of the patients rated Dr. Campbell in one of the lower categories – that's 5.13 patients out of the 38 who completed the survey. If Dr. Campbell sees 20 patients per day and works 4.5 days per week, the findings suggest that, each week, 12 patients don't think that Dr. Campbell met their service expectations. Using Humana's ratio, these less-than-loyal patients could account for 24 to 36 neutral or negative comments to friends and family members.

DATABASE COMPARISONS

The next three pages of Dr. Campbell's report contain a series of bar graphs that convert the percentage responses into mean scores that can be compared with other databases. For Question A1 ("Ease of making appointments by phone"), we can see that the doctor's current mean score (4.46) is lower than his previous score (4.56), but he ranks in the top half of SuperCare Medical Group (4.41) and well above the mean score of the Dermatology database (4.32).

By themselves, survey scores are only a snapshot – they provide a point-in-time measurement. When the current score is compared with a previous one, and with the group's mean score, you can say something important to Dr. Campbell: Although his score ranks in the top half of all the doctors in the practice (and higher than the database), it's lower than it used to be. Reviewing the benchmark comparisons, Dr. Campbell should ask himself why his score for Question A1 is trending downward – e.g., what might have happened in his practice to cause the lower score – and what he can do to raise the score by the next survey.

STATISTICAL SIGNIFICANCE

In comparing survey scores, Dr. Campbell will want to know if the differences are significant. In normal English, "significant" means important, while in statistics "significant" means *probably true* (not due to chance). When statisticians say a result is "highly significant" they mean it is very probably true. They do not necessarily mean it is highly important.[7]

We'll leave a more detailed discussion of statistical significance to the experts; the "Statistical Significance of the Differences in Mean Scores" analysis in Appendix C shows what happens when the computer is asked to calculate significance for each survey question. In the example, the right-hand columns indicate which scores are significantly higher (or lower) than the database used for benchmarking – in this case, comparing current scores with the scores received on your previous survey.

SPECIAL REPORTS FOR ANALYZING SERVICE PERFORMANCE

Appendix C contains two reports which practice managers find useful in analyzing the data and setting priorities for creating a culture of service.

The *Provider Ranking Graph* on page 119 compares all physicians (and mid-level providers) in the practice, ranked according to their average scores for Section D of the survey ("Your Visit With The Provider"). These questions are useful in comparing the doctors to one another because they represent areas over which the provider has control – as opposed to process issues like "waiting time in reception," which is a system affected by many other factors. For practices that have an incentive program for physicians, a Provider Ranking Graph shows who the superstars are, and which doctors need special attention (please see Chapter Nine for ways to help low-scoring physicians).

The *90th Percentile Mean Comparison* on page 118 shows where the score for each survey question ranks in the benchmarking database and the score needed to rank in the top 10 percent of the database. For example, the mean score for Question C1 ("Your phone calls answered promptly") is 3.91 – which ranks at the 23rd percentile of the database (second column), well below the database mean score of 4.1 (fourth column). The mean score in the third column shows the score needed to rank in the top 10 percent of the benchmarking database (4.65).

You can use the 90th Percentile Mean Comparison analysis as a way to set improvement goals. For example, a correlation analysis indicates that Question B3 ("The caring concern of nurses/medical assistants") has a big effect on "Overall satisfaction with our practice" (F1)—so you might conclude that raising the score for B3 is a good idea. The current mean score is 4.44 (40th percentile). You could shoot for the 90th percentile (4.77), but that might be too far to go by your next survey. Using the 50th percentile as your goal (4.46) might be too easily achieved, so you might set your next target somewhere around 4.57 as a realistic goal for your nurses and medical assistants.

The advantage of setting quantified goals is obvious. Instead of exhorting people to "run faster and work harder," you can set a clear target that the nurses and medical assistants can accept, and everyone will know when they reach it. You'll find that people are more willing to follow your lead if they have a definite goal to shoot for. What's more, it gives you a reason to celebrate when they hit the target.

OTHER ASSESSMENT STRATEGIES

A patient survey is your most valuable measurement tool, but it's not the only way you can obtain useful information about your service strengths and weaknesses. Two additional ways are mystery patient assessments and key-person interviews.

Mystery patient assessment

While patient surveys have the advantage of allowing you to solicit opinions among large groups of patients, they also have the disadvantage that the questioning is not very deep. Patients circle answers on the rating scale, but their response doesn't tell you anything about the specifics behind the scores.

Your tool for digging deeper into the strengths and limitations of your practice is the mystery patient assessment. A professional "shopper" – often a person with direct experience working in a medical group – calls for an appointment, goes through the entire encounter, and sends a full report of the experience. Mystery patients tell you where your practice shines and where it needs polishing. The report exposes exactly what happens during a normal patient encounter and pinpoints the reasons behind the survey scores. The recommendations help you make specific changes to the work processes and physician/staff performance that increase patient satisfaction.

Appendix D on pages 120–123 contains a typical checklist used by mystery patients to report on the specific aspects of the encounter. Each section allows for comments, as lengthy as needed, and conclusions regarding how likely patients are to stay loyal and refer others to your practice.

Typically, mystery patient reports are confidential. They are sent or presented in person to the practice manager, who decides how the results will be shared with physicians, supervisors, and staff members. (As you might expect, specific comments in the report can arouse defensiveness on the part of the "shopped" physicians and staff if they are broadcast to everyone in the practice.) The report will include the positive aspects of the visit, not just the areas that need improvement. Issues affecting physicians can be reviewed with the president or medical director, who decides what action to take. Issues affecting employees would be shared with appropriate supervisors.

You'll also want your entire team to know how they're doing as a group. At intervals, you can produce a summary report of all mystery patient assessments. Names and departments can be edited out to avoid shining a negative spotlight on individuals; after all, the assessment is about your entire practice as a team. If it's true that "we're all in this together," then it doesn't matter which person or department the report is about.

As one administrator put it: "If someone praises you, I get to walk in your sunshine; if someone criticizes me, you'll all be tarred with the brush."

Another benefit of mystery patient assessments is this: Whereas a patient survey usually is conducted once or twice each year, during which time physicians and employees can "polish their act," *an assessment can occur at any time*. Nobody knows when or where the mystery patient will visit, which keeps everyone's attention on service all year round!

This qualifies your mystery patient program as part of the momentum strategy we'll discuss in Chapter Nine, except that we'll also describe a way that you can organize and manage the program yourself, without having to pay for professional mystery patients!

Key-person interviews

Your own people are also a source of valuable assessment information; they see what happens on a daily basis, and often have the best ideas about potential solutions.

We might add that talking with your key people brings them into your strategies for improvement. People who are asked for their input are more likely to support an action plan than those who feel excluded from the assessment process.

You can address both of these issues by adding a schedule of key-person interviews to the preparation for a Customer Service Initiative. Partner physicians, supervisors, and employees can all give you an insider's perspective on the challenges they face every day and their insights regarding things to improve. Insiders can report on "what works and what doesn't." Supervisors can provide detailed feedback on performance areas where employees do well and where they don't. Frontline and support staff can add their perspective on teamwork and the working conditions that affect their ability to meet or exceed patient expectations.

Key-person interviews can be one-on-one or in focus groups. You can review the findings of the patient survey and mystery patient assessments and ask your colleagues to comment on the issues raised. A workable interview checklist might contain the following questions:

1. What do you think patients like best and least about our practice?

2. Where do you think we excel at meeting patients' service expectations? Where do we fall short?

3. What's your biggest challenge when you're trying to deliver top-level service to our patients?

4. What usually happens when you hear about a patient who is unhappy with our practice? How do you feel we perform when things go wrong?

5. If you could make one change to improve patient satisfaction, what would it be?

ASSESSMENT REPORT

Now it's time to assemble a report that will be the basis for setting priorities and building a Customer Service plan. You have the patient survey, mystery patient assessments, and key-person interviews to work from. It's time to designate the people who will be responsible for integrating all the input into a single report.

Let's call them the Customer Service Committee. And you're in charge of nominating the people who will serve on it; whom will you choose?

If you manage a small practice, you might want everyone to be on your committee. For larger practices, you might consider a committee that represents a cross section of the practice – physicians, someone from the administrative team, supervisors of key areas, and one or two staff members with seniority and a reputation for participating constructively in meetings.

We should note that forming a Customer Service Committee has its own potential pitfall: If the committee members lack sufficient "rank" in the practice, they'll have difficulty getting the attention of senior leadership for their conclusions and recommendations. More than a few Customer Service Initiatives have lost their momentum because responsibility was delegated to people who, although committed, were unable to gain the attention of the practice leadership team.

So you have an assessment report. The question now is, how do you convert what you've learned into an implementation plan that will galvanize the organization toward service excellence? That's where we're going in the next chapter.

CHAPTER FIVE

Step Two:
Involving the Leadership Team

"No problem can withstand the assault of

sustained thinking."

VOLTAIRE

Ever wonder why so many plans end up on the shelf?

That question has perplexed business leaders since the 1940s, when managers first entertained the notion that greater productivity could lead to increased profits without adding to overhead expense. They tried a number of planning strategies to increase productivity, most of which ended up partially implemented in the dustbin.

A plan is a road map, and if your Customer Service Initiative is to survive beyond the initial fanfare, you'll need one. Without a plan, your only tools for promoting ongoing patient-centered performance are speech-making and arm-twisting. (Like Sunday sermons, speeches have a tendency to be forgotten by midweek.)

Years ago, after moderating dozens of Board retreats and helping physicians convert their mission/vision statements into multiyear business plans, we were dismayed to check back and learn how few of the planned activities had actually been put into action. There seemed to have been plenty of enthusiasm at the start, but Board members reported that in the aftermath of the retreat, other factors had intervened to push the plans to back burners.

No wonder so many Board retreats are looked back upon as academic exercises.

So we studied the factors that inhibit the success of action plans, and what we learned may surprise you.

WHAT'S WRONG WITH TRADITIONAL PLANNING

Picture the way planning usually takes place. Somebody thinks that an objective is important enough to merit a formal approach for reaching it. A small group is formed to do the homework and produce the plan. The task group works in isolation, and some people even forget it's going on.

Then, one evening at a partner meeting, the full plan is unveiled in a tab-divided binder choked with background, research findings, and recommendations. A few people ask questions, and everyone is satisfied that the task group did its job. The planners ask for an up or down vote of approval. With no chance to preview the material in detail, the partners vote yes, because it seems like a good thing to do, and the task group appears to have thought its way through the options.

The problem is, no one "owns" the plan except the folks who built it!

No wonder the task group finds less than willing cooperation when it tries to implement the action steps. Some people who understood little more than the basic outlines balk when they learn that the changes will affect them personally – "I didn't know you meant *that*!" Some gripe because they felt left out of the planning process – "I could have told you, if you'd asked me." Others see themselves as exceptions – "Go ahead and make your changes; just leave me out of it!" Still others simply turn away and hope nobody will hassle them about it.

So the implementation lumbers along, with peaks of achievement and valleys of disappointment, often to the tune of detractors who were lukewarm toward the plan in the first place – "I told you it wouldn't work!"

We found that, in medical groups, the principal reason that action plans fail is the "disconnect" between the planners and the physicians, supervisors, and employees whose buy-in is vital for the plan to succeed.

Your customer service action plan deserves a better fate.

A NEW WAY TO PLAN FOR CUSTOMER SERVICE

The story is interesting, but it's a long one, so here are the highlights. In the 1950s, reliability engineers in several U.S. industries were frustrated because their productivity plans weren't achieving the goals they had set. Some objectives were met, while others weren't. Some things went smoothly, while others didn't, and nobody knew why or what to do when things went wrong.

At the same time, they knew from their own project work that most plans – even the ones that failed – were sound. After all, humans are geared toward positive action, and the plans had been designed by intelligent people who knew what was needed. Whatever shortfalls occurred were not caused by lack of effort. The engineers concluded that the plans failed not because people didn't know "what had to happen," but because they didn't give enough attention to "what could go wrong" – and what they would do if it did.

They needed a new approach – one that would accomplish two objectives:

- Anticipate both what needs to happen and what could go wrong
- Build champions and supporters by involving all the people charged with implementing and supporting the plan.

Their idea led to a dramatically different planning process that (a) increased the likelihood of succeeding by reducing the probability of failing; and (b) created part-authors of the plan by including as many people as possible in the process.

They realized that to be successful, a plan needs both success enhancement *and* failure avoidance. And being engineers, they felt most comfortable reducing the concept to a formula; this is what it looked like:

$$P_{(s)} + P_{(f)} = 1.0$$

In this formula, the probability of succeeding, $P_{(s)}$, plus the probability of failing, $P_{(f)}$, always equals one. If true, then there are two ways to give an action plan its best chance – either *increase the likelihood of succeeding* by asking "what has to happen for us to achieve the goal?" or *lower the possibility of failing* by considering "what could go wrong as we implement the plan, and what will we do if that happens?" Second, to build champions and supporters for the long haul, they needed a structure that would include everyone whose buy-in and support were necessary for success.

Why go into all this detail? Because the strategy was so successful in industry that it soon attracted the attention of health care organizations. Mayo Clinic used it to plan its entry into the Scottsdale market. Palo Alto Medical Foundation (Calif.) used it to plan implementation of electronic health records. Bright Medical Associates (Whittier, Calif.) used it to fend off an unfriendly takeover and reorganize its governance and operations. The process was so effective that some people referred to it as "fail safe."

The challenge was to involve physicians and managers without taking them too far away from their daily jobs. They're busy people who can't be involved in a lengthy process at the expense of seeing patients or managing work units, or give up what remains of their personal lives in a series of off-hour meetings. So the planning process also had to be relatively quick and easy.

THE LEADERSHIP ACTION PLAN

"Avera/Avera McGreevy Clinic (Sious Falls, S.D.) is an integrated practice with more than 50 physicians and five practice sites," according to John Healy, Vice President of Primary Care. "We needed to enlist every member of our group in a team effort to raise our patient survey scores, and we wanted to do it fast."

Armed with a detailed baseline service assessment, John invited 30 stakeholders to participate in a half-day planning session – Board members, partners and associates, administration and key department heads, and some first-line supervisors.

"In less than four hours, we had our plan," John says. "Now we're implementing it, with the active involvement of the same people who built it."

Here's how they used the "fail-safe" planning process to increase the likelihood of succeeding while reducing the probability of failing.

Prework

An invitation to the planning meeting was sent to all parties. Accompanying the invitation were an explanation of how the planning process would be conducted and a summary of the baseline assessment findings, so that everyone could come prepared to contribute.

Planning work session

Everyone had reviewed the baseline service assessment. The planning session was held on a weekday morning. After the moderator previewed the planning agenda, the remainder of the work session was devoted to building an action diagram that, before they started, looked like Exhibit 5.1 on page 54.

It's called a "decision-tree diagram" and links the goals with objectives that must be met and the tasks needed to accomplish the objectives. The process began with the entire group agreeing on a goal statement – to raise "overall satisfaction with our practice" from the 76th to the 90th percentile within one year (to be measured by a patient survey in the first quarter of 2007).[8] The goal-setting process took about 30 minutes, and the diagram now looked like Exhibit 5.2 on page 55.

With the goal established, the next task was to determine the objectives ("what has to happen" to achieve the goals). The entire group brainstormed for approximately one hour and settled on the objectives shown in Exhibit 5.3 on page 56.

The next task was to list the action steps ("what has to happen" to achieve each objective).

Satisfied with the objectives, the planners continued to build the decision tree diagram. They divided into separate teams, each of which listed the tasks needed to achieve each objective. In just over an hour, each team completed the third part of the diagram and returned to present its recommendations to the full group. Questions were answered, and revisions were made to reflect the input. The action diagram, as shown in Exhibit 5.4 on page 57, was now complete.

The group was now into the third hour of the action planning process, and a final step remained – anticipating "what could go wrong," and deciding what to do if it did.

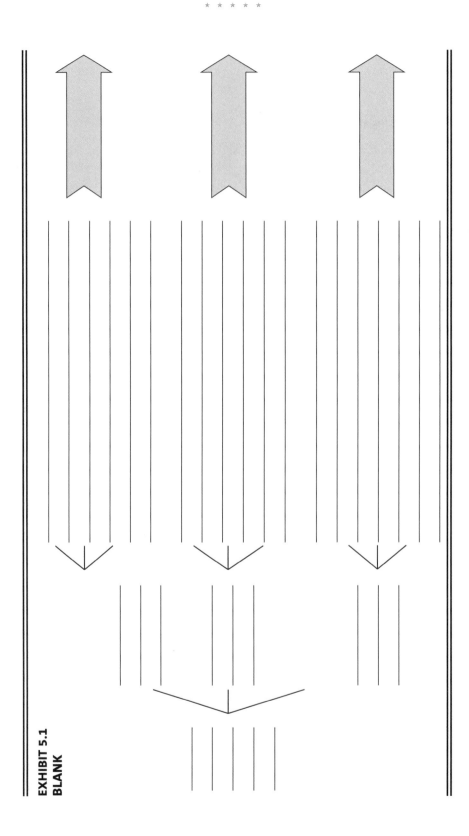

EXHIBIT 5.1
BLANK

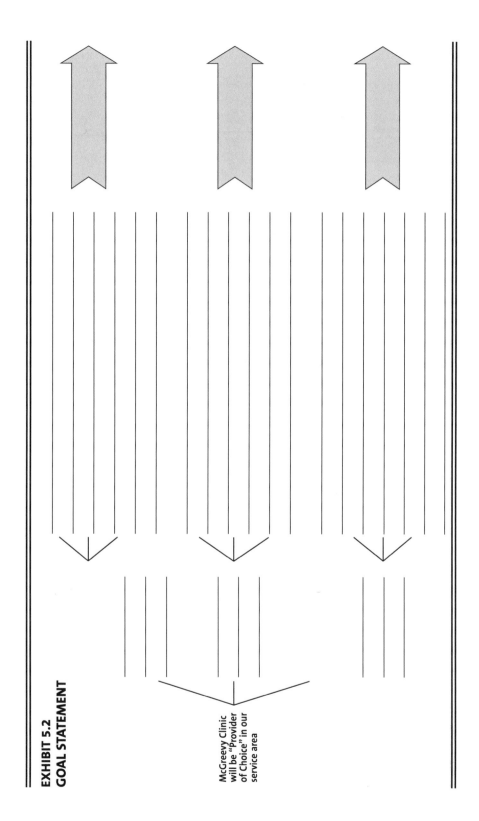

EXHIBIT 5.2
GOAL STATEMENT

McGreevy Clinic will be "Provider of Choice" in our service area

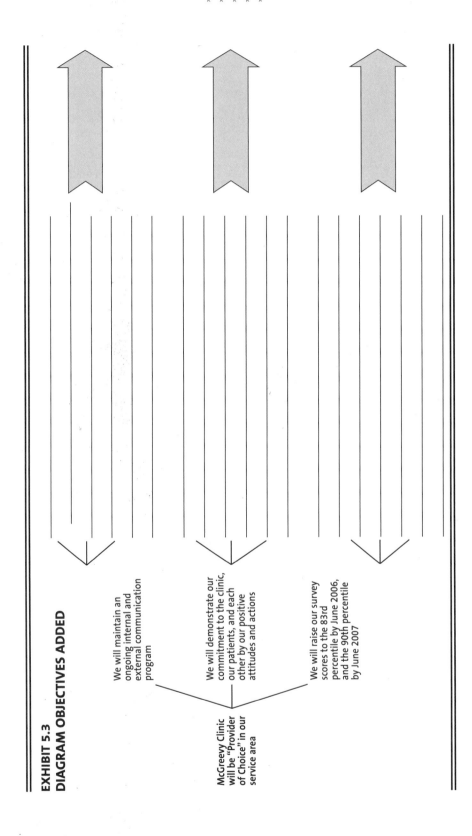

EXHIBIT 5.3
DIAGRAM OBJECTIVES ADDED

McGreevy Clinic will be "Provider of Choice" in our service area

We will maintain an ongoing internal and external communication program

We will demonstrate our commitment to the clinic, our patients, and each other by our positive attitudes and actions

We will raise our survey scores to the 83rd percentile by June 2006, and the 90th percentile by June 2007

**EXHIBIT 5.4
COMPLETED**

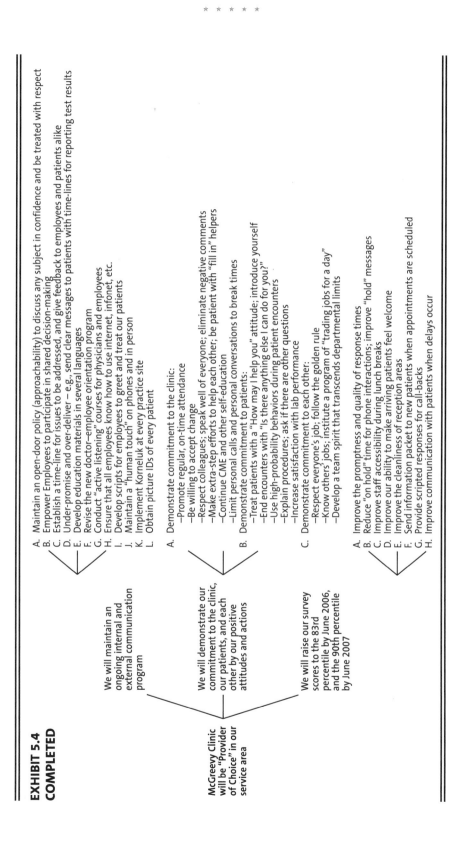

McGreevy Clinic
will be "Provider
of Choice" in our
service area

We will maintain an
ongoing internal and
external communication
program

A. Maintain an open-door policy (approachability) to discuss any subject in confidence and be treated with respect
B. Empower Employees to participate in shared decision-making
C. Establish a time-line for issues to be addressed, and give feedback to employees and patients alike
D. Under-promise and over-deliver – e.g., send clear messages to patients with time-lines for reporting test results
E. Develop education materials in several languages
F. Revise the new doctor–employee orientation program
G. Conduct "active listening" courses for physicians and employees
H. Ensure that all employees know how to use internet, infonet, etc.
I. Develop scripts for employees to greet and treat our patients
J. Maintain a "human touch" on phones and in person
K. Implement Korneluk at every practice site
L. Obtain picture IDs of every patient

We will demonstrate our
commitment to the clinic,
our patients, and each
other by our positive
attitudes and actions

A. Demonstrate commitment to the clinic:
 –Promote regular, on-time attendance
 –Be willing to accept change
 –Respect colleagues; speak well of everyone; eliminate negative comments
 –Make extra-step efforts to help each other; be patient with "fill in" helpers
 –Continue CME and other self-education
 –Limit personal calls and personal conversations to break times
B. Demonstrate commitment to patients:
 –Treat patients with a "How may I help you" attitude; introduce yourself
 –End encounters with "Is there anything else I can do for you?"
 –Use high-probability behaviors during patient encounters
 –Explain procedures; ask if there are other questions
 –Increase satisfaction with lab performance
C. Demonstrate commitment to each other:
 –Respect everyone's job; follow the golden rule
 –Know others' jobs; institute a program of "trading jobs for a day"
 –Develop a team spirit that transcends departmental limits

We will raise our survey
scores to the 83rd
percentile by June 2006,
and the 90th percentile
by June 2007

A. Improve the promptness and quality of response times
B. Reduce "on hold" time for phone interactions; improve "hold" messages
C. Improve staff accessibility during lunch breaks
D. Improve our ability to make arriving patients feel welcome
E. Improve the cleanliness of reception areas
F. Send information packet to new patients when appointments are scheduled
G. Provide scripted responses for call-backs
H. Improve communication with patients when delays occur

In a group discussion, the planners considered major obstacles and counter-strategies.

Aftermath

The action diagram was distributed to every physician, department head, and supervisor in the McGreevy organization. The Customer Service Committee made additional revisions as the implementation proceeded and highlighted "critical paths" as action steps were completed.

SUCCESS SCENARIO

The decision-tree planning process was used by the physicians and managers of Buenaventura Medical Group. Within eight months, a follow-on patient survey showed some dramatic results. Of 33 questions, 28 showed statistically significant improvement, including the all-important question "Your overall satisfaction with our practice," which climbed 24.6 per-centile points!

"The action diagram was more than a work plan," according to Susan Graham, Buenaventura Medical Group's Vice President of Human Resources. "The Customer Service Committee also used it to keep track of our progress, and to keep the imple-mentation process moving along when things were happen-ing more slowly than we wanted, or if obstacles arose to inhibit our momentum."

BUENAVENTURA MEDICAL GROUP
PATIENT SURVEY SCORES – August 2005–April 2006
(Scale 1–5)

	BEFORE	AFTER
Your appointment	3.94	4.10
Our staff	4.38	4.46
Our communication with you	4.04	4.16
Your visit with the provider	4.41	4.54
Overall satisfaction	4.36	4.46

During the same period, average scores for Buenaventura physicians rose from the 46th to the 80th percentile of the multispecialty database. Similar increases were seen in nearly every other performance dimension.

"This was the most effective technique I had seen for obtaining consensus on a fairly intricate plan," says Dr. Manuel Marquez, Medical Director. "In an amazingly short time, we all had a chance to speak our minds and hear the rationale behind the action steps. We were confident that our decisions were sound and would be supported once we outlined the plan at partner and site meetings."

Businessman and visionary John L. Beckley is credited with coining the phrase, "Most people don't plan to fail, they fail to plan." We agree. Without a carefully crafted plan and the buy-in of practice leadership, all your good intentions are little more than wishful thinking. Physicians and managers can work together, in less time than it used to take, to build a road map which the entire organization can follow. And the "star-studded" results at Buenaventura Medical Group, accomplished in less than a year, speak for themselves.

The Action Diagram also implies that people will be held accountable – but accountable for what? Our next chapter addresses the issue of defining service protocols and communicating them to every physician, manager, and employee in your practice.

CHAPTER SIX

Step Three:
Defining Service Protocols

> *"It is a funny thing about life;*
> *if you refuse to accept anything but the best,*
> *you very often get it."*
>
> W. SOMERSET MAUGHAM

Why do we have two different ways of managing people? Why one way for clinical and procedural tasks performed by staff members and another way for the service aspects of the job?

In medical practices, clinical and procedural standards are well defined. Everyone knows what the standards are and that meeting the standards is not an option according to what kind of day the employee is having. For example, there is a specific, well-defined procedure for nurses when drawing a blood sample, and all the nurses know it. One of the steps is to swab the area where the needle will be inserted with an antiseptic solution. This is a requirement, not an option – nurses do not skip the swabbing if they're running behind, or having a bad day.

Another example is when patients arrive for check-in. Every receptionist knows that the correct name or birth date must be entered to "bring up" the appropriate record from the computer files; there's no tolerance for getting this information wrong, and mistakes are quickly rectified.

In both cases, employees who fail to meet performance standards are corrected and counseled, and supervisors watch closely to make sure that performance changes immediately to meet the standards. In fact,

repeated omissions or errors can become issues for oral or written warn-
ings, probation, and even termination if performance doesn't improve.

Ask the same nurses about customer service, say, what they do for
patients who are afraid of needles, and you might get a different answer
from every nurse in the building. That's because the best way to handle
anxious patients is *not* standardized. Every nurse may have a favorite
technique, and too often, not everyone knows the best way. Further,
some nurses may know the best technique, but might vary or skip it if
they're rushed.

For lack of a clear definition, we tend to generalize about customer service. Too often, when survey scores are lower than desired, we exhort people to do their best without a clear definition of what "best" is! Instead of
specifics, you might hear something like "Our recent survey scores are
lower than we'd like, and we know that patient satisfaction is important,
so let's all re-double our efforts to do better."

These early attempts to build "service excellence" in medical groups were
little more than motivational pep talks. Managers would convene an in-
service meeting, emphasize that "professionals care about service, too,"
and exhort employees to do their best. As a consequence, employees
couldn't be faulted for concluding that service is a good thing, and worth
doing "if things are going right and I have the time."

Trouble was, those motivational pep talks raised momentary awareness,
but they rarely changed behaviors on a lasting basis. Physicians and
employees accepted the service argument on an intellectual level, and
their performance would improve for a while, but pretty soon things
would slip back to normal in the face of crowded schedules, ringing
phones, and a mandate to overfill every slot in the schedule.

If we don't tell people what we want, then we'll have to content ourselves
with whatever we get. Unless, of course, we *could* define service in behavioral terms that everyone understands and accepts. Then every nurse
would know the best technique for dealing with patients who fear a needle, just as they now know the best way to take a blood sample. And what
if you communicated this technique, not as an option, but as a required
part of the job – in fact, a condition of employment?

Physicians, also part of the delivery system, came by a different route to conclude that service is a secondary consideration. Their medical training focused on the *science* of medicine (that subject took all the training time they had!) to the exclusion of service as an intrinsic part of doctoring. Once they entered the "real world" of solo and group practice, they might have read about it in a medical journal, or heard someone mention the subject of service at a partner meeting.

With an education built on diagnosis and treatment, and collegial governance that emphasized personal autonomy, the result was predictable. Physicians couldn't be blamed for concluding that medical excellence not only trumped all other considerations, but that patient satisfaction wasn't all that important in the course of making an accurate diagnosis and providing excellent treatment.

In this chapter we'll discuss the process for defining service protocols – specific job requirements that deliver star-studded service – and a strategy for communicating them to every member of the team.

SERVICE SCENARIO

In Chapter Four we saw the value of mystery patient assessments. Not too long ago, one of our project leaders placed a mystery patient phone call to a small practice, in preparation for customizing the staff training seminar. She asked to speak with one of the physicians.

"He's with a patient," the medical assistant answered. "I'll let him know you called."

That's a fairly standard response, and every word is truthful. The medical assistant correctly tells the patient that the doctor is busy in the exam room. She does intend to give him the caller's message, and she knows that at some point the doctor will return the call.

But let's stop for a second and reflect on what the caller understands as a result of what she heard the nurse say. Patients know approximately how long their visit usually lasts – they've probably been to the doctor before – and the caller can't be blamed for assuming that the doctor would return the call when he finished with his current patient, perhaps as soon as 20 or 30 minutes later.

The doctor telephoned the caller two hours and forty minutes later.

If the caller had been a "real" patient, and if the practice had received a satisfaction survey, the score for Question C6 ("Our ability to return your phone call in a timely [within two hours, on the same business day, within 24 hours] manner") would most likely have been less than an "Excellent" rating. The patient had expected a return call within the hour, and her expectation was not met. The unconscious comparison patients make when answering survey questions is to mark the difference between what they expected, and what they got.

What if the medical assistant had phrased her message differently? Suppose she had said, "The doctor's with a patient just now. He has two more waiting, and he normally returns calls between eleven o'clock and noon. Is that okay?"

If it's not okay, the patient is probably in an emergent situation, and a quick callback would be necessary. But most patients will accept the answer. When the doctor calls back in a few hours, he will have met the patient's expectations. In the second example, the medical assistant's answer helped the patient set an expectation that the doctor could meet *without changing his process for managing the morning schedule.*

You might wonder, how would a medical assistant come up with a "script" like the second message noted above? You'd be fortunate if it were instinct; it's more likely that the "script" was proposed because it's a better way to handle the call.

DEFINING SERVICE EXPECTATIONS

If physicians and employees are going to deliver Star-Studded Service, they're entitled to know what's expected of them. It isn't enough to say "let's all do our best," as if everyone already knows what "best" is, and a pep talk is all that's needed to galvanize them into action. When performance falls short of expectations, it's often due to a lack of clearly defined service standards.

We could spend a lot of time discussing how you would go about building a set of customer service standards – assembling a development team, brainstorming behavioral standards, writing and revising the drafts, and so on. However, there's a better and faster way – we'll share the service protocols we use when we work with single- and multi-specialty clients to install the six-step Customer Service Initiative.

A word of caution, though: *Consider the following protocols as only a starting point.* They're better than starting with a blank sheet of paper, but they don't reflect the specific issues and challenges of *your* practice. You'll still need to revise or add to them to reflect your special requirements based on your size, specialty, or competitive position in your service area.

Protocol 1: *Make a great impression*

It's not paradoxical to say that the first impression is the last impression. Satisfaction with the medical encounter starts as the patient enters your practice – a friendly, upbeat welcome sets the tone for everything that follows. If the first few minutes make a negative impression, your back-office staff will have to work twice as hard to undo it.

Here's what you're up against: Many seasoned, frontline employees appear "on autopilot." It's easy to understand how this could happen – receptionists, nurses, and medical assistants are continuously confronted by unpredictable workloads, variability in patient expectations, lean staffing, and limited resources. Moreover, the task of "making a great first impression" is repetitive, and good people can simply "retreat to process" to get through their workday.

The net effect is a feeling that people are going through the motions without much spark. Most frontliners – not knowing what to expect from arriving patients – appear to adopt a neutral facial expression and speak in a neutral tone of voice. Yet most brighten immediately if our mystery patient takes the initiative, for example, by complimenting them or saying something funny.

The point is this: you can't afford to have patient-contact people who wait for *the patient* to initiate a friendly exchange. Receptionists, nurses, and medical assistants – in fact, anyone who interacts with patients and caregivers – have to take the initiative, even though they might risk being "shot down" by a grumpy patient.

Here are four basic protocols, each of which correlates with higher survey scores that you can share with your staff:

1. Acknowledge patients and caregivers immediately; make eye contact and smile.

2. Let patients know if delays are expected; keep them informed of their status.

3. Use simple, nontechnical language whenever possible.

4. Be patient in answering questions; make sure the information is understood.

Protocol 2: *Be a telephone superstar*

When you're answering the phone, you're at a disadvantage. Behaviorists know that about 65 percent of people prefer to take in information visually; only 38 percent use hearing as their primary means of receiving information. On the phone, there is no visual contact, which means that tone of voice and message content are your only tools for making callers feel valued and important.

Here are six protocols that your employees can use during phone calls:

1. Answer the telephone with a friendly, helpful tone of voice.

2. Ask if you can put callers on hold; wait for an answer.

3. When returning to the line, thank the caller for holding.

4. If you cannot help immediately, take the caller's name and number and say when you'll call back.

5. When taking messages, repeat the information to confirm the details.

6. End the call with "Is there anything else I can do for you?" and a friendly good-bye.

Protocol 3:
Handle the reception room with caring professionalism

Sarah arrived six minutes early (10:24 a.m.) for a 10:30 a.m. appointment. She spent two minutes in the check-in line and was advised to "have a seat and we'll call you." It's now 11:10 a.m., and there are five patients sharing the reception area.

Suddenly the door to the clinical area opens, and the medical assistant calls Sarah's name. Sarah responds and almost makes it before the door starts to close, because the medical assistant (MA) is already walking down the hall. After a quick "good morning," they arrive at the scale.

"Don't look at my weight," Sarah says, joking to cover her distress at having gained a few holiday pounds. "I have to write it down on your chart," answers the MA.

On the way to the exam room, Sarah tries to recall the employee's name. The name badge is not helpful because it's hanging at the end of a lanyard, in the general region of the MA's beltline and turned so that it's facing inward.

Once seated in the exam room, Sarah knows what's coming next as the cuff is placed on her bicep. The MA begins pumping up the pressure. "What's my blood pressure?" Sarah asks as the cuff is removed. "Sorry, the doctor will have to tell you that," is the MA's response as she moves toward the door saying "The doctor will be with you shortly."

Any reason to doubt that Sarah feels like she's been "processed" rather than welcomed? Rooming patients starts with a warm hello and an apology if Sarah has been waiting more than 15 minutes past her appointment time. If your medical assistants use the behaviors noted below, there's a good chance that whatever dissatisfaction was caused by the waiting time will dissipate as Sarah is made to feel welcome.

1. Step into the reception area when calling patients; wait for him or her to reach the doorway.
2. Smile, introduce yourself (if appropriate), and say something pleasant.
3. On leaving the exam room, tell the patient how long the wait will be.
4. Check back with patients every 10 minutes with a status report.
5. Minimize small talk with other employees within the patient's hearing range.

Protocol 4: *Say good-bye when patients and co-workers leave*

If you took Latin courses in school, you may recall why the verb is always placed at the end of the sentence. It's because the Romans believed that readers would remember the last part of a statement better than what was said at the beginning. Because the verb carries the meaning of the sentence, they wanted it to be remembered.

In the same way, the last thing that happens during a medical encounter often influences how patients feel about their experience. With physicians, their behavior when exiting the exam room is a primary factor affecting the patient's feelings about whether the doctor has spent "enough time with me." For staff members, patient departure is a perfect opportunity to reinforce the welcome message.

> Adding two more protocols for your back-office people will raise your patient survey scores:
>
> 1. Before the patient leaves, ask – "Did you get all of your questions answered?"
>
> 2. Make a friendly parting comment, such as "Bye now," "Take care," or "Nice to see you."

Protocol 5:
Handle complaints in a responsive and professional manner

Did you know that a dissatisfied patient gives you a wonderful opportunity to create a willing and enthusiastic "ambassador" for your practice? That's because researchers who study consumer attitudes have learned an important theorem: If you can persuade me that (a) you care as much about my problem as I do, and (b) you're determined to make things right for me, I'll become *more loyal to you* than if the problem had never occurred!

That's amazing! It means that unhappy patients are not just irksome interruptions to an otherwise placid day; they represent a marketing opportunity to promote positive referrals that are often expressed as "Something went wrong, but I was impressed by how well they reacted to my problem."

So converting a negative situation into a positive one is a good thing to do. But why wait until a patient lodges a complaint? Studies show that only 1 of 20 unhappy patients will voice their displeasure – the other 19 will simply "vote with their feet" and bad-mouth your practice to their friends.

The time for your employees to respond to a dissatisfied patient is not when they hear the complaint, but when they see the frown. That's when they can take the initiative by saying something like "You seem upset . . . is there something I can do for you?" Once the complaint is out in the open, here are five protocols that will convert frowns into smiles:

1. Respond to questions and complaints in a positive and helpful manner.

2. Let the person know that you're interested in solving the problem.

3. Apologize for the inconvenience; don't respond with arguments or excuses.

4. Listen for the facts; let the person tell the whole story.

5. Describe what you plan to do, and follow through.

Protocol 6: *Be a cooperative and helpful team member*

We've all heard the expression "Together Everyone Achieves More," which stands for "TEAM." It's true. People who work well as a team are more productive, and they tend to enjoy their jobs more than those who don't have a "family feeling" about their workplace.

But what exactly is a team? How do you know if your employees really are a team? And if they aren't, how might you go about creating a team?

Much has been written about team building, most of which focuses on concepts for changing people's attitudes toward each other, and that's fine. We'd also argue that you can build teamwork by defining the behaviors you want to see when you watch your employees at work. Consider the following protocols:

1. Arrive at your workstation and be ready to begin work at the start time.

2. Recognize that everyone's job is important.

3. Treat requests from other employees as priority issues; keep your promises.

4. Don't criticize colleagues in front of patients or fellow employees.

5. Follow the dress code; wear your name badge correctly.

6. Maintain patient and organizational confidentiality.

7. Limit personal phone calls and small talk; don't let personal remarks be overheard.

Like all performance standards, the service protocols represent the *minimum* you expect from your staff – they're a floor, not a ceiling. At the same time, meeting these standards is a sure-fire way to raise your scores on patient surveys. Each of the protocols listed above has been shown to correlate closely with the criteria patients use when answering survey questions like those on the MGMA-Sullivan/Luallin survey form (see Appendix A). If every member of your team demonstrates these behaviors every day with every patient, your next survey scores are sure to be well above the 50th percentile of the benchmarking database.

SUCCESS SCENARIO

"At Elkhart Clinic [Elkhart, Ind.] we take the protocols a step farther," according to Roger McCann, Assistant Administrator. "Our Customer Service Committee offers scripts to employees who might encounter patient displeasure."

For example, the Committee knew that some patients object to the repetitive questions asked when receptionists update the information files. The advice is to "explain to patients that it's to their advantage if the demographics are up to date – that is, mail can be sent to the correct address, the doctor will be able to contact them, and their claims will be filed correctly."

The Committee wrote a script to cover this situation: "I'm going to ask you some questions and it may seem that we're asking these questions more often than necessary, and I apologize for that. However, we've found that sometimes things get changed in patient accounts, or we may have entered your information in error. So we review your account information on a regular basis."

In another case, when receptionists determine that a patient must be sent to the business office on matters relating to their account, the advice is to prevent patient agitation or frustration by saying, "I really am not the best person to talk with, and I don't want to give you any incorrect information. I'm sure our patient financial representative will be able to answer any questions you may have."

SCRIPTING FOR SERVICE EXCELLENCE

If you like Elkhart Clinic's approach to scripting, here's an assortment of scripts that have been proven effective:

Telephone

Switchboard - "Good morning, _____Medical Group, how may I direct your call?"

Internal call - "Internal Medicine, this is Nancy, may I help you?"

Need to hold - "May I put you on hold please?" Wait for answer (repeat if necessary).

Unable to hold – "May I have your number and I'll call you back within ____ minutes."

Returning to the caller – "Thank you for your patience. How may I help you?"

Transfer call - Words/process depends on phone system.

Transfer to voice mail – "Thank you. Can I transfer you to her voice mail or would you prefer to leave a message with me?"

Patient appointment scheduler – "May I have your name please?" [pause for response] "Thank you, [insert patient name]. May I have your date of birth, please?" [pause for response] "Thank you." Schedule appointment, reconfirm appointment date and time, and confirm which doctor.

New patient – "Do you know where we're located?" Give directions and offer to send a map.

End of call - "Is there anything else I can help you with?"

If no - "Thank you for calling _____Medical Group."

Patient greeting (registration/reception)

Greeting – "Hello, may I help you?" (Smile with your voice!)

If busy - Make eye contact and acknowledge person (even person second in line).

Other employees in registration/reception area – Acknowledge and smile.

New patient - "I see you're a new patient. Welcome to _____ Medical Group. Do you have a patient handbook?"

Collect copay – "How would you like to take care of your copay today?"

"The doctor is running _____. Please have a seat in the reception area and Mary Beth will be calling you when the doctor is ready."

If the doctor is more than 25 minutes behind – "I'm sorry for this inconvenience, would you like to re-schedule?"

Reception Room

Nurse – step into the reception area, and call patient's name. Wait for him or her to reach the doorway before turning around. Lend assistance if necessary.

Smile, introduce yourself (if appropriate), and say something pleasant to the patient, "Good morning, Susan. How's the weather outside?"

New patient – acknowledge – "I see you're a new patient. Welcome to _____ Medical Group (or physician's practice)."

Take vitals – share results with patient.

On leaving the room say, "Doctor _____ has one other patient ahead of you. It will probably be 10 minutes before he comes in. Is there anything I can do for you while you wait?"

New patient – "It was good to meet you. If you ever have any questions, please feel free to call me." (Write your name on doctor's card and give to patient.)

Check back with patient every 10 minutes to inform of provider status.

Patient Departure

Last person to interact with patient – "Did you get all of your questions answered?" Direct patient where to go next (checkout or other department).

Parting comment – "Take care."

WHAT ABOUT YOUR PROVIDERS?

If physicians and mid-level (nonphysician) employees are also part of the delivered product, then doesn't it make sense to apply the same logic to them as we do to employees? Several medical groups have extended the concept to their physicians, reasoning that doctors are an inseparable part of customer satisfaction.

SUCCESS SCENARIO

"Several factors combined to prompt the development of physician guidelines," says J. Michael Schwab, administrator of The Portland Clinic (Portland, Ore.). "By the mid-1990s our service area had seen rapid growth in managed care, which led to tighter profit margins and pressures from HMOs to raise the quality of patient care. Further, a large influx of physicians had descended on the Portland area – at one point there were 35 percent more physicians than our population needed, which meant that the supply of doctors had grown faster than the demand for their services.

"To stimulate patient-centered performance, we first had to change the compensation formula to reward the providers who did the best job of satisfying existing patients and attracting new ones. With graduated incentives, the Board wanted to give every physician an equal chance to excel – by publishing guidelines that, if properly applied, would produce high survey scores.

"The guidelines were divided into six areas of performance: practice patterns, patient relations, cooperating with other physicians, leadership qualities, partnership standards, and professionalism."

Mike reports that defining provider standards contributed to The Portland Clinic's growth in market share. "Our doctors responded to both the guidelines and the use of patient survey scores for determining incentives. Between 2002 and 2005, our mean score for 'Overall satisfaction with our practice' rose from 4.54 to 4.70, which ranked our practice above the 77th percentile of the multi-specialty database; during the same period, our physicians raised their aggregate mean scores from 4.61 to 4.71. Both increases are statistically significant."

THE IMPORTANCE OF PHYSICIAN COOPERATION

Why the emphasis on physician performance? There are three answers, and we'll spend some time explaining them because *enlisting the willing cooperation of your physicians is essential to a successful Customer Service Initiative.*

Bringing physicians into your program can be a challenge because, on most patient surveys, the physician scores are higher than those for the other sections of the survey. Seeing themselves at the top of the scores, physicians might logically conclude that they don't need to be part of your Initiative – "We're the highest scorers, so we're not your problem. You should put your efforts into improving staff performance and work processes."

So here are three arguments you can make for physician participation in the Customer Service Initiative.

Physicians are the centerpiece of the medical encounter

Patient satisfaction with the physician is the most important component of "Overall satisfaction with our practice," Question F1 on the MGMA-Sullivan/Luallin patient survey form. The correlation analysis on the following page proves the point. Exhibit 6.1 shows the beta coefficients for

EXHIBIT 6.1

PRIMARY CARE DATABASE
CORRELATION ANALYSIS

E2.	Overall comfort	0.739
C3.	Explanation of your procedure (if applicable)	0.710
D6.	The thoroughness of the examination	0.709
D5.	Instructions regarding medication/follow-up care	0.704
D1.	Willingness to listen carefully to you	0.697
D2.	Taking time to answer your questions	0.696
C2.	Getting advice or help when needed during office hours	0.691
D4.	Explaining things in a way you could understand	0.691
D3.	Amount of time spent with you	0.684
C5.	Effectiveness of our health information materials	0.681
D7.	Advice given to you on ways to stay healthy	0.681
E1.	Hours of operation convenient for you	0.672
B3.	The caring concern of our nurses/medical assistants	0.671
C6.	Our ability to return your calls in a timely manner	0.666
A3.	Getting care for illness/injury as soon as you wanted it	0.660
B1.	The courtesy of the person who took your call	0.651
C4.	Your test results reported in a reasonable amount of time	0.645
A9.	Ease of getting a referral when you need one	0.644
E4.	Signage and directions easy to follow	0.644
B4.	The helpfulness of the people who assisted with billing or insurance	0.640
B2.	The friendliness and courtesy of the receptionist	0.639
C7.	Your ability to contact us after hours	0.637
A5.	The efficiency of the check-in process	0.634
C1.	Your phone calls answered promptly	0.625
A4.	Getting after-hours care when you needed it	0.618
C8.	Your ability to obtain prescription refills by telephone	0.615
B5.	The professionalism of our lab or X-ray staff	0.611
A2.	Appointment available within a reasonable amount of time	0.599
A8.	Keeping you informed if your appointment time was delayed	0.596
A1.	Ease of making appointments by phone	0.588
A7.	Waiting time in the exam room	0.585
A6.	Waiting time in the reception area	0.565
E3.	Adequate parking	0.521

MGMA-Sullivan/Luallin Primary Care Database – July 2006

every survey question in our national Primary Care database. As we explained in Chapter One, beta coefficients express the relationship of specific survey questions with a dependent variable (F1). The threshold for statistically significant correlation is a beta of 0.500; anything higher is significantly correlated with "Overall satisfaction with our practice." Exhibit 6.1 shows:

- For primary care practitioners, the responses to *all* survey questions have a significant effect on overall satisfaction.

- Seven of the top eleven beta coefficients involve satisfaction with the provider.

Physician scores affect every other survey score

The second reason is even more persuasive: Physicians cannot ignore the "halo effect" of their scores on the remainder of the patient survey – a fact that was proven in a study of 16 physicians at Beaver Medical Group.

Here's the background. Competing in the lively Southern California market, Beaver Medical Group needed to maintain patient loyalty, both for "pay for performance" incentives and for protecting its existing revenue base from new competition. Knowing that physician scores were highly correlated with overall patient satisfaction, the partners decided to give special help to the providers ranked in the bottom quartile of the patient survey. Sixteen of the 18 lowest-ranked physicians agreed to undergo a "shadowing" consult as a means of improving their scores. (More about "shadow coaching" in Chapter Nine.)

Two weeks later, a "pulse" survey was conducted for the 16 physicians, with predictable results: the doctors had improved their summary scores from 3.99 to 4.24, which ranked them collectively at the 44th percentile of the group.

The real surprise, however, was the effect that higher physician scores had on overall satisfaction with the practice and the quality of medical care. Exhibit 6.2 shows that both of these scores increased in direct proportion to the rise in physician scores.

And that's not all. The improvement in doctor performance *lifted all other scores in the patient survey* as shown in Exhibit 6.3, even satisfaction with parking!

EXHIBIT 6.2
BEAVER MEDICAL GROUP
PULSE SURVEY – 16 SHADOWED PHYSICIANS

	BEFORE	AFTER
Overall satisfaction with our practice	4.02	4.27
Overall rating with the quality of your medical care	4.10	4.34

The implications of this "halo effect" are enormous.

- Physicians who say that customer service is a matter for administration and staff are losing sight of their importance to overall patient satisfaction. Even when the scores for Section D of the report are high, the Beaver study proved that physicians cannot be exempted from the Customer Service Initiative.

- Management can save time and money by raising physician scores. For example, if you want to raise your score for "wait time in the exam room," you could spend countless staff-hours forming an improvement team, flowcharting the process, brainstorming solutions, implementing and measuring, and so on. The Beaver study shows that BMG raised its score for Question A7 from 3.42 to 3.62 simply by raising physician mean scores from 3.99 to 4.24.

EXHIBIT 6.3
BEAVER MEDICAL GROUP
PULSE SURVEY – 16 SHADOWED PHYSICIANS

	BEFORE	AFTER
A2. Appointment available in reasonable time	3.48	3.73
A4. Getting after-hours care	3.67	3.72
A5. Efficiency of the check-in process	3.99	4.22
A6. Wait time in reception	3.38	3.68
A9. Ease of getting a referral	3.90	4.21
C1. Phone calls answered promptly	3.64	3.68
C4. Test results reported in reasonable time	3.67	3.84
C8. Obtaining prescription refills by phone	3.81	3.95
E3. Adequate parking	3.59	3.75

Physician performance is under the microscope

The third reason why physicians need to maximize their patient survey scores is to protect their eligibility to participate in contracts with health maintenance organizations (HMOs) and other payers. Much payer effort is currently being expended in a drive to obtain provider-specific data. The reason behind this effort is becoming clear: Payers are increasingly intent on "driving" their members toward physicians who score high on "quality" measurements, one of which is patient satisfaction. In some markets, payers are already reducing copays for members who visit "preferred" providers. If this tactic proves successful, we can expect to see it employed in major markets nationwide.

Recognizing the implications of these multiple market forces, many larger groups have set "service guidelines" for physicians mirroring the "service protocols" they impose on employees. Among the leaders in this regard is The Care Group (Indianapolis, Ind.), where a physician task group was formed to develop guidelines for more than 80 cardiologists. Appendix E on pages 124–126 contains physician guidelines which The Care Group has used since 1991 as a factor in its annual physician incentive formula.

This chapter may have seemed longer than it needed to be; however, our experience is that defining service expectations in specific ways is indispensable if your Customer Service Initiative is to succeed in the long run. Expectations are your foundation for converting the service "sermon" into an ongoing management system. And if everyone knows specifically what's expected of them, you'll have a much better chance of achieving the dual objectives in maintaining the loyalty of current patients and generating word-of-mouth referrals.

Having defined your expectations for customer service, the next step is to ensure that every member of your team has the skills and techniques they need to meet the standards you've set. That's the message of our next chapter.

CHAPTER SEVEN

Step Four: Patient-Pleasing Techniques

"Winning is not a sometime thing ...
you don't do things right once in a while,
you do them right all the time. Winning is a habit.
Unfortunately, so is losing."

VINCE LOMBARDI

Winning seasons begin in training camp. Coach Lombardi knew that his "boys" were already professionals who had demonstrated the instincts for football mechanics – otherwise, they wouldn't have been on the payroll. He also knew that champions excel at the *basics* of the game, which explains why his training camps were notorious for endless repetitions of basic plays and basic techniques. Under him, the Green Bay Packers won two Super Bowls and three consecutive league championships. (Guess Vince knew what he was talking about!)

It's the same with training for customer service. If you're looking to create a "service culture" that demonstrates consistent, star-quality treatment of patients and their family members, you'll need an effective training strategy that enables physicians and employees to deliver it.

Larger practices can choose from a variety of training companies – some better than others – to deliver the service message. The best of these companies tailor the content of the seminars to the specific issues and challenges confronting the practice; the worst of them propose generic training programs that work in any service industry.

The average MGMA member manages a smaller-size practice, with one or two sites and fewer than a dozen providers. If you fit that category, your budget might be stretched beyond practicality by hiring outsiders to handle the service training of your physicians and employees.

So let's assume that your strategy is to do the training yourself. How can this book give you the tools, even though you're not a training professional? Can you persuade your colleagues that customer service makes good business sense, and give them proven techniques for meeting the service expectations of your patients and referring physicians?

To answer these questions, let's first agree that, just like the Green Bay Packers, you already have the "basics" of customer service. The preceding chapter is replete with examples of service protocols for staff members, and The Care Group has given you an excellent list of service guidelines for providers. Using these techniques has been proven to promote high patient survey scores. So the challenge is to use the protocols and guidelines as centerpieces of your training seminars.

CUSTOMER SERVICE FOR PROVIDERS

A recent customer service seminar had attracted more than 80 physicians at a large multispecialty group. Nearly all were upset that their patient survey scores were trending downward, and some were eager to hear how they could protect their dominant market position.

To demonstrate the need for physician involvement in the improvement strategy, the seminar leader reviewed the rationale for customer satisfaction. Halfway through his remarks, he was interrupted by an internist who was ready to change: "Just tell us what to do," she said.

That's where you come in. You can play a pivotal role in your Customer Service Initiative.

You've done your homework, and you know that at least a few of your doctors understand the importance of patient satisfaction and are committed to excelling at customer service. You also know that some of your physicians are neutral about this subject – either they believe that medical quality is all that's necessary or they may be resentful that market forces have intruded on their desire for autonomy. Either way, you know that there'll be proponents and antagonists in your customer service sem-inar – some will be looking for "what we should do," while others will still be in a "prove it to me" mood.

THREE-STEP STRATEGY FOR CONDUCTING A CUSTOMER SERVICE SEMINAR

To conduct a customer service seminar for providers that will achieve your objectives, here's a strategy consisting of the following three steps:

1. Preparation

2. Seminar outline

3. Post-seminar reinforcement

Preparation

Every provider should come to your seminar prepared for the service message. Along with the announcement, send each participant a copy of your most recent patient survey report – both the summary report for the practice and the provider's individual report. You might also send a per-tinent article on customer service from any *MGMA Connexion* magazine. (For example, Appendix F contains an article from MGMA's annual pub-lication, *Practices and Performance of Successful Medical Groups*, which out-lines a workable strategy for achieving high survey scores.)

Seminar outline

An outline for the seminar follows.

A. Provide the rationale for achieving customer satisfaction by reviewing the following benefits of meeting/exceeding patient expectations:

- Patient loyalty and referrals;

- Higher morale and clinical department productivity;

- Better risk management;

- Strong negotiating position with payers;

- Pay-for-performance incentives;

- Better public image;

- Better medical outcomes; *and ultimately* more career satis-faction for physicians!!

B. Give a brief picture of how you're doing by focusing on the following in your patient survey:

> • Question F1 ("Overall satisfaction with our practice")
>
> • Section B ("Our Staff")
>
> • Section D ("Your Visit with the Provider")
>
> • Use the 90th Percentile Analysis to show where your practice ranks in the database.
>
> • Give a general report of assessment findings (self-directed mystery patient assessments; please see Chapter Nine).

C. Start a discussion of *why* the doctors think the survey scores aren't higher, and what they think can be done to raise them.

> • This discussion is very important; your doctors are highly competitive individuals. They want to please patients and are frustrated when their survey scores indicate otherwise. Remember that service was not part of their medical training and they may be encountering the notion of customer satisfaction for the first time.

D. Use the remedial suggestions in Appendix H on pages 132–140 to suggest techniques doctors and staff members can use to increase patient satisfaction.

E. Give everyone a copy of the "Quick Reference Guide."

> • The Quick Reference Guide contains behavioral techniques that any provider can use, regardless of personality or attitude, to make patients feel valued and important. The recommended techniques are grouped according to specific questions on the patient survey. With practice, they can easily become part of how your providers relate to patients, even on the busiest day of the year.

Some physicians fear that changing their practice patterns to satisfy patients' service expectations will lengthen the visit and further complicate their workday. You can assure them that the techniques in the Quick Reference Guide, Exhibit 7.1, can be used without adding time to the exam room encounter.

EXHIBIT 7.1

PATIENT-PLEASING TECHNIQUES FOR PROVIDERS
QUICK REFERENCE GUIDE

D1. Willingness to listen carefully	– Get on eye level (as soon as possible) – Maintain eye contact – Take notes as patient speaks – Ask if patient has other issues to discuss
D2. Taking time to answer questions	– Get on eye level (as soon as possible) – Maintain eye contact – Smile (when appropriate) – Ask if patient understands
D3. Amount of time spent with patient	– Warm, friendly handshake – Relaxed posture/attitude – End visit with shoulder-pat, handshake – Let patient exit first (if possible)
D4. Willingness to explain	– Get on eye level (as soon as possible) – Maintain eye contact – Smile (when appropriate) – Apologize for being behind schedule – Let patient finish answering questions
D5. Giving instructions	– Get on eye level (as soon as possible) – Maintain eye contact – Ask if patient understands
D6. Thoroughness of the exam	– Tell patient what's going to happen – Give findings/results as you go – Pay attention to caregiver, too
D7. Advice given on staying healthy	– Explain chart references – Review instructions; ensure understanding
General techniques	– Knock on exam room door before entering – Use patient's name

Post-seminar reinforcement

Prepare a handout containing the agenda items covered in the seminar, and distribute it to the doctors as a reminder of what was discussed and decided. Include the providers who could not attend. In your cover letter, promise that everyone will be kept informed of activities, progress, and future assessments, including the results of your next benchmark patient survey.

A final thought: During employee seminars on customer service, some-one usually asks, "Have the doctors heard this?" If you have conducted the provider seminar outlined above, you'll be able to say yes, and that answer will be a powerful motivator for your employees.

CUSTOMER SERVICE FOR STAFF MEMBERS

Few of us are motivational speakers. That's okay, because the following four-step strategy does not rely on pep talks to get your message across. In fact, your approach is solidly grounded on business precepts – defin-ing service expectations and promising to hold people accountable for meeting/exceeding them.

Preparation

Send every staff member an "invitation" memo describing the impor-tance of customer satisfaction and the purpose of the seminar.

Seminar outline

Repeat steps A and B from the provider seminar.

Part of your team-building strategy is to acknowledge that employees are an indispensable part of the customer service effort and, as such, they're entitled to know why service is important and how the practice is doing. However, be judicious in selecting the amount of information you con-vey. For example, while you reviewed the survey data in detail with the providers, you can avoid defensiveness on the part of employees by mak-ing general comments about the survey results, e.g., using only the sum-mary scores from each section of the survey.

Get everyone thinking about service

As an introduction, you can help your employees put themselves in the customer's place by reading the following vignette, and asking them to stop you every time they hear something that does not represent good customer service.

> *A frail, elderly lady approaches the counter. Carrie, the receptionist, chat-ting on the phone, is gazing off into the distance.*

"You're kidding!" she says, "I can't believe she wore that to a wedding!! Listen, I gotta go, there's someone here."

The receptionist hangs up, looks at the woman and says, "Yes?"

"I'm Mrs. Johnson. My doctor sent me here for some kind of test," says the lady with a nervous tremor in her voice.

The receptionist, looking a little irritated says, "You're late." She checks the schedule and notes the woman is in for a sigmoidoscopy.

"Did you get your prep taken care of?" she asks.

The old woman, a little hard of hearing leans forward and says, "My what taken care of?"

"Your prep, you know, your enema," replies the receptionist in a voice loud enough to be heard throughout the reception area.

Ask the group how this elderly patient will feel about her encounter with Carrie and what she's likely to say to her friends and family members.

Review the service protocols

Discuss each of the protocols listed in Chapter Six (or as you've amended them to reflect the specific needs of your practice). Use examples from your own experience to illustrate why the protocols are necessary. *Explain that the protocols will be added to everyone's job description and used in the annual performance appraisal for each member of the team.* This is the critical point to make – you don't want your employees to see this meeting as just another informational briefing. The key is to position Star-Studded Service as "the way we're going to do business, from now until forever."

And don't worry that your employees will resent having service protocols as well-defined components of their jobs. In fact, we believe that all employees (and their bosses, for that matter) have two unalienable rights – first, to know what's expected of them; and second, to know how they're doing. The protocols respect the first of these rights; the second is fulfilled in daily coaching and annual performance appraisal.

Follow-on reinforcement – the "pizza lunch"

In the weeks following the seminar, schedule a series of lunches for your entire staff. At each meeting, use the outline as shown in Exhibit 7.2 to lead a discussion of a specific protocol:

EXHIBIT 7.2

STEP	ACTIVITY	REMARKS
1	Schedule meeting	Set date/time when interruptions are at a minimum
		Choose a place that's quiet and away from office bustle
2	Announce meeting	Send "invitation" memo
		Answer questions as appropriate
3	Facilitate meeting	Describe how the service strategy applies to your department
		Review the specific service protocol for the day
		Ask how the protocols apply to their jobs (discussion)
		Ask what could prevent meeting the protocols; how to avoid
		Tell the group you'll be watching
		Emphasize that service is not an isolated "promo of the month"
4	Preview	Tell the group you'll discuss other protocols at the next meeting

Please notice that the "pizza lunch" is different from other meetings you normally conduct with your staff. For one thing, it's a discussion rather than a place for you to speak and everyone else to take notes. The idea is to involve team members in practical discussions of what's expected, what obstacles may arise to hinder their efforts, and what everyone can do to keep the focus on patient satisfaction as a continuing way of doing business.

AND WHAT ABOUT YOU?

Here's how important you are. When our company is retained to conduct customer service seminars, we schedule 90 minutes for the providers, two hours for the staff, and a full day for managers and supervisors!

That's because, in our view, managers have the toughest job in a medical practice. Physicians can tell everyone what to do; employees can sit back and ask, "What do you want me to do?" Managers are in the middle, having to satisfy everyone's needs and the myriad interruptions that arise to spoil an otherwise well-planned day. Further, a manager's span of authority is often poorly defined – you can get into trouble today for doing something that was perfectly acceptable yesterday. Not to mention the challenge of working with physicians who aren't always agreed on a course of action – satisfying one doctor might antagonize another.

There are many excellent courses and manuals that address the multiple roles of managers, all of which make the point that getting things done through others is a highly complex process requiring skills in planning, organizing, motivating, and controlling the performance of others. The full subject is well beyond the scope of this book. Still, there are a few issues we might discuss to help you manage for service excellence.

Role modeling

Your exhortations regarding customer service can be undermined if you are not seen as practicing patient-centered behaviors yourself. The service protocols apply to you first, in the decisions you make that affect how patients and caregivers view your practice. When staff members see your commitment, they know you're serious about patient satisfaction and that you hold yourself as well as them accountable for results.

Correcting unsatisfactory performance

It takes special skills to change people's behavior while still keeping them on the team. You have the power of your position – because you outrank all other employees, your word carries weight and you have the authority to back up your decisions and actions. However, there are rules about using your power:

- You must have power in the first place – your power base is your physicians, and smart managers always check to see that planned actions will be supported.
- You must be seen as willing to use your power – setting rules without enforcing them is a recipe for leaving employees in charge of their actions.

When you use your power you must be perceived as fair, objective, and focused on the goal – which means that (a) your rules must apply to everyone regardless of seniority or job position; (b) you must administer those rules consistently to avoid being seen as playing favorites; and (c) your decisions must be seen in light of the objectives of the Customer

Service Initiative, not as arbitrary reflections of whatever mood you're in at the moment.

That said, here is a list of performance-correcting techniques that might make the difference between effective and ineffective management:

EXHIBIT 7.3

SEVEN RULES FOR
CORRECTING UNSATISFACTORY PERFORMANCE

1. Don't let the sun go down!	Problems get worse if you leave them alone.
2. Praise in public; criticize in private.	When you praise people in public, you get more of the desired behaviors; when you criticize people in front of others, you get defensiveness.
3. Control the emotional temperature.	It's OK to reflect the severity and number of times the unacceptable behavior has occurred.
4. Focus on behavior, not attitudes	Talk about what you see, not about why the person might have behaved that way.
5. Deal with specifics, not generalities.	People can't make changes unless they know what behavior is unacceptable, and that specific changes need to be made.
6. Set new standards and deadlines.	Say exactly what behavior you will accept and how long you're willing to wait for improvement.
7. Let people know when their performance is satisfactory.	This is the step we all forget about!

BE AN EFFECTIVE LEADER

Leaders are not born; they become leaders by having high standards, and holding themselves to them. Exhibit 7.4 shows our recommendation for the performance standards that should accompany *your* job description.

EXHIBIT 7.4

PERFORMANCE STANDARDS FOR MANAGERS

A. DEMONSTRATE EFFECTIVE MANAGEMENT SKILLS

1. Show support for the organization's mission and goals.
2. Hire qualified staff; ensure that new employees are oriented and trained.
3. Organize the workload; establish standards to ensure productivity.
4. Demonstrate knowledge of all duties of staff members.
5. Motivate staff to ensure that performance standards are met or exceeded.
6. Conduct fair, objective performance appraisals by the appropriate deadline.
7. Give timely, constructive feedback on performance; document all counseling.
8. Demonstrate effective problem solving; resolve issues, implement solutions.
9. Demonstrate knowledge of established policies and procedures.

B. DEMONSTRATE EFFECTIVE LEADERSHIP QUALITIES

1. Motivate staff to take responsibility for the quality of their work.
2. When delegating tasks, clarify the desired outcomes.
3. Encourage suggestions from staff members.
4. Ensure that in-service education is available within budget constraints.
5. Publicly recognize good performance; give constructive criticism in private.
6. Keep staff aware of changes in organization and department policies.
7. Be a role model in demonstrating the service standards.
8. Ensure teamwork/cooperation between your staff and other departments.

C. MAINTAIN A HIGH DEGREE OF PROFESSIONALISM

1. Demonstrate a high degree of personal integrity.
2. Demonstrate a high commitment to the success of our practice.
3. Be willing to make decisions and take action.
4. Recognize new situations; find ways to maintain productivity and morale.
5. Be willing to accept new responsibilities.
6. Demonstrate an ability to be effective in stressful or changing conditions.
7. Model teamwork; attend meetings, and be prepared to participate.

We're now finished with our discussion of Step Four in your Customer Service Initiative. This is the point where many service efforts stop, with the predictable consequence that momentary enthusiasm fades over time and eventually, things return to "normal."

To maintain the momentum of your program for Star-Studded Service, you need a tracking system that keeps everyone in the practice informed of the progress they're making and the results they're achieving. That's the subject of the next chapter.

CHAPTER EIGHT

Step Five:
Tracking Mechanisms

> *"What gets measured gets managed.*
> *What is managed gets better."*
>
> TOM PETERS

Training without accountability is wishful thinking.

Drive down Main Street during the United Way annual fund drive. Somewhere you'll see a billboard with an appeal for support, usually with a thermometer that shows the progress toward its current fund-raising goal. For good measure, you'll see the same message on posters in the windows of banks and barber shops.

That's because United Way knows something about reaching goals, financial or otherwise: If you keep showing people the progress they're making, they're much more likely to help you reach your goal.

It's the same with your Customer Service Initiative. At the start, your physicians and employees may know that patient satisfaction is important, and they'll probably share your frustration that patients aren't happier with the services they receive. The action plan (Chapter Five) got everyone involved in setting goals and identifying "what has to happen" to increase patient loyalty and referrals. In the seminars (Chapter Seven) you introduced protocols and guidelines that were welcomed with varying degrees of enthusiasm and support. Now you need a "booster" strategy for letting everyone know that service goals are achievable and they're making progress toward achieving them.

You can use several benchmarking strategies to keep your colleagues informed of progress.

FOLLOW-ON PATIENT SURVEYS

The ultimate measuring stick is the patient survey itself; it's your best tool for knowing that your efforts to meet patients' service expectations are producing results. Most practices survey once or twice each year; however, if your score for Question F1 ("Your overall satisfaction with our practice") is in the lower quartiles, you may feel a need for more frequent measuring.

SUCCESS SCENARIO

Clearwater Cardiovascular and Interventional Consultants (Fla.) offers a good example of how the frequency of surveying can be adjusted to reflect changing needs. "We had been surveying our patients annually," according to Fred Simmons, Executive Director. "In the mid-1990s, we were anticipating significant changes – closing an office and opening a new one, making new arrangements with our hospitals, and consolidating our operations in various ways. We wanted to know as soon as possible if any slippage would occur in our services. The Board decided to conduct quarterly surveys during the transition, and to review the findings at meetings of our partners and staff members. This way, we were able to address problem areas in real time."

The entire transition process took 18 months, after which, Fred and his team resumed to a schedule of annual surveys.

SELF-DIRECTED MYSTERY PATIENT PROGRAM

Physicians and employees are observant. They know when a patient survey is being conducted and when the process is over. It's possible for them to "polish their act" while the spotlight is shining, and focus on other priorities once the surveys are distributed and the report is published.

Mystery patient assessments can be conducted at any time, targeting any physicians or practice sites you'd like. The problem is, hiring outside consultants to make phone calls and visits can be expensive. The self-directed strategy costs nothing – it can be administered by insiders, using your own patients!

Here's how it works. You (or someone serving on the Customer Service Committee) contact a patient scheduled for an office visit in the next few weeks:

> "Hello, this is Charlie Perkins from SuperCare Medical Group. We understand that you have an appointment with Doctor Brown next Thursday, is that right? Great, and we're glad you chose our practice.

> "Perhaps you'd like to be part of our mystery patient program. All our doctors and staff know about this program, and we use the reports to identify what you like about our practice, and where we should make improvements. It's a very important program for us. Would you be willing to be a mystery patient for us?

> "Terrific! I'll send you an information packet, with instructions and a simple survey form. All you need to do is answer the questions after your visit and send it back to us in the reply envelope. Is that okay?"

The materials for the information packet are contained in Appendix G on pages 130 and 131. Please notice that the report form is simpler than a patient survey, which asks for evaluations on a five-point scale; it's a one-page questionnaire with all questions requiring a "yes/no" answer.

It's important that your physicians and staff do not see the mystery patient report as a witch hunt – its purpose is *not* to root out "bad apples" or to give your people a hard time. The objective is to give your clinical and support teams an interim report on how they're doing toward the improvement goals they've set for themselves (please see the discussion of team rewards in the next chapter). Used in this fashion, the mystery patient reports will be seen as helping mechanisms, instead of a punitive program that shines the spotlight on their weaknesses.

And best of all – it's free!

OTHER TRACKING SYSTEMS

You have several other information sources for keeping track of progress:

- Requests for records transfer
- Letters from patients
- "Storyboard" project reports
- Service spotlight memos

Requests for records transfer

Patient departures are always troubling, but they give you an excellent opportunity to conduct telephonic "exit interviews." In minimal time, you can learn whether the reason for departure is benign (change of health plans, moving to another city, and so on), or if the move was prompted by dissatisfaction with your practice.

Letters from patients

Anecdotal notes and letters are powerful, whether they're complimentary or critical, they represent firsthand feedback with tremendous credibility. When patients write positive letters, they often identify specific individuals as service standouts; these comments can be posted on bulletin boards and included in your interim reports. Negative comments usually give specific reasons for dissatisfaction; they can be shared in confidence with specific individuals and departments as an indicator of performance areas needing attention.

"Storyboard" project reports

To address a particular problem (e.g., long wait times in reception), the Customer Service Committee may have designated a project team to implement improvement strategies that require the cooperation of several members of the practice. Their work can be summarized and presented at partner meetings or distributed to all doctors and employees. You don't have to be "fancy" with the report; a simple description of the project will suffice:

- The initial problem
- Improvement goal

* * * * *

- Flow chart of the current process
- Results of brainstorming possible solutions
- Implementation strategy
- Results achieved

"Service spotlight" memos

Superstars love recognition. Extra effort can be published as examples for everyone through memos from your desk, complimenting people who make extra efforts to satisfy patients.

SUCCESS SCENARIO

Years ago, Honolulu Medical Group (Hawaii) did a great job in this regard. In the physician/employee lounge (yes, doctors and staff took their breaks in the same area!), there was a bulletin board and, nearby, a supply of hand-shaped papers with the notation:

"I think [_____] deserves a pat on the back because [_____.]"
There were no rules – anyone was entitled to complete the form and affix it to the bulletin board with a thumb tack. The result was astounding – physicians wrote complimentary messages about staff members, and vice versa. And everyone who visited the lounge could read them. This was among the most effective team-building strategies we've seen!

The Customer Service Committee can obtain other sources of information that measure service performance: malpractice claims, referring physician surveys (if yours is a specialist group), staff turnover, and others. Our point is that regular progress reports not only keep your team members informed – they also stimulate better service performance by reinforcing your commitment to patient satisfaction as a continuing way of doing business.

Practice managers can use three additional strategies to maintain the momentum of the Customer Service Initiative, and they're important enough to deserve chapter-level treatment. Please read on, and you'll learn about your most important tools for "holding the gains" and sustaining the effort toward patient-centered performance.

CHAPTER NINE

Step Six:
Momentum Strategies

*"But I have promises to keep . . .
and miles to go before I sleep."*

ROBERT FROST

George Rogers Clark and Meriwether Lewis set off with great fanfare. Behind them were the charter from President Jefferson and a proclamation from the Congress. Eastern newspapers lauded their journey to find a Northwest Passage as the doorway to the country's future. They left St. Louis with cheers and good wishes from civic leaders and ordinary citizens. It must have been quite a send-off.

Days later, the landscape was uninspiring and the sun was hot. The food was stale and the excitement of starting out had been replaced by dull routine. The pioneers had more than 1,500 miles to go!

Customer service initiatives can be that way. The enthusiasm of the physicians, the interest in the action diagram, the improvement by shadowed providers, the confidence that service protocols will increase patient satisfaction – all can fade as your people return to the daily grind of input and throughput. As weeks turn into months, performance can return to preinitiative levels.

Like the Lewis and Clark expedition, your "journey" toward Star-Studded Service can lose momentum. It would be nice if the techniques taught in training seminars would have a life of their own, and that once learned, they would become part of physicians' and employees' daily performance. We know better; managing for patient-centered service does not follow the rules of other business systems – without reinforcement, all your efforts to improve patient satisfaction and raise your survey scores can diminish in the endless routine of daily workloads.

THREE MOMENTUM STRATEGIES

There's hope. Large group practices, especially those competing for health plan "pay for performance" incentives, have instituted three key strategies that help keep the momentum created by the first five steps of our strategy. They know that maintaining the momentum is more critical than ever, in light of new payer initiatives to measure "quality" at the provider level and offer their members "tiered copay" options in which patients save out-of-pocket expense by choosing preferred physicians. (A recent quote from the Remington report says it well: Pointing to a $10 to $15 copay differential between the physician "tiers," the editors advise that "all providers should expect patient satisfaction surveys as a quality performance measure.")

So what are the top scorers doing, and how can their strategies be adapted in smaller practices to raise patient survey scores?

Managers: making rounds for service excellence

You have a full desk. Your in-basket is loaded with requests you must respond to and problems you must solve. There are issues you must study and reports you must write. And plenty of reasons why you should stay in your office, all day long, and you still wouldn't run out of practice management issues.

But you can't do that – not if you want your Customer Service Initiative to survive and thrive. Like doctors who "make rounds" when they have hospitalized patients, you need to visit your front and back offices several times each week to interact with physicians and staff, see what problems they're having, reallocate resources to plug your weak spots, and generally let everyone know that their efforts are appreciated.

You can also provide structure for your "rounds" – the pizza lunches described in Chapter Eight can be used to address issues as they arise, enlisting feedback from the folks on the front line, and eliminating obstacles to customer service.

In particular, you're being watched closely by every member of your team. Role modeling for Star-Studded Service means that when alternative options have an effect on patient satisfaction, decisions favor the options that lean toward satisfaction.

Our observation is that as managed care took hold in recent decades, the contracted arrangements prompted management decisions aimed more at satisfying payers than meeting the service expectation of patients. That was then. Responding to the consumer trends mentioned in our opening chapters requires a new focus on patients, rather than on the coverage they carry. Preferred provider organizations (PPOs), individual health savings accounts (HSAs), and employer attempts to shift premium costs to their work forces – all these trends argue for a return to the way medical groups behave in fee-for-service markets. This issue is an indispensable subject for every partner strategic planning retreat.

Shadow coaching for low-scoring physicians

In most practices, a few physicians receive complaints from patients, bottom-quartile survey scores, or patient requests to change providers. These physicians are frustrated; they don't know why their patients are dissatisfied and most of them will welcome help to improve their performance.

Lack of "positive affect" between provider and patient also affects the quality of medical care. Research conducted since the 1980s has shown that when patients "like" their doctor, they tend to be more cooperative in following the treatment plan – taking all the medicine, showing up for follow-on appointments, sticking to diets, and so on. As a consequence, these patients have better medical outcomes.

Shadow coaching is a new concept in which a physician receives a full day of observation and feedback from an experienced consultant, with the focus on specific techniques that enhance the patient/provider encounter. Here's how it works:

1. The "lead" physician (president or medical director) contacts the provider, reviews the record, and offers a day of shadowing as a helping mechanism to improve patient interactions.

2. If the provider agrees, the shadow coach telephones to explain the process and answer questions. (We've found that physicians who

resent the intrusion, or are otherwise resistant to shadowing, are not good candidates for this service.)

3. The shadow coach arrives a few minutes before the start of an office day's schedule to meet the provider and staff, answer any remaining questions, and preview the day's activities. The coach also dons a lab coat.

4. With each patient, the physician introduces the shadow coach as preparing a report on "a day in the life of a doctor," and asks permission for the coach to observe the encounter. (The coach steps out of the exam room if the provider senses any discomfort on the patient's part.)

5. Throughout the morning schedule, the coach observes the provider's performance and the subtle reactions of the patient, noting specific words and actions affecting satisfaction.

6. The lunch break is devoted to a detailed discussion of the provider's performance during the morning appointments, noting strengths ("what you did right"), as well as areas where "you can do better." The coach suggests specific techniques to concentrate on during the afternoon schedule.

7. Throughout the afternoon, the coach discusses progress in the hallway between encounters, noting observations and making further suggestions.

8. The shadow day concludes with a brief wrap-up meeting, during which the provider helps to develop a personal action plan.

Within two weeks of the shadowing, a "pulse" survey is taken to measure the before-after difference in patient reactions to the provider's attempts to promote "positive affect" during encounters. The results are confidential, shared only with the provider and, perhaps, the "lead" physician.

The results at Beaver Medical Group, when 16 bottom-quartile physicians were shadowed, are presented in Chapter Six. Their aggregate score for Question F1 ("Your overall satisfaction with our practice") increased from 3.99 to 4.24, which placed them at the 44th percentile of the Primary Care database.

SUCCESS SCENARIO

Further evidence comes from Dr. Marc Greenwald, Chief Medical Officer of Fallon Clinic (Worcester, Mass.). "From our patient survey we recognized that there was a group of physicians who consistently scored lower than their colleagues. We scheduled the shadowing as a detailed observation of physician performance, with feedback related to customer service – in both physician/patient interactions and physician/staff collaboration."

All the physicians agreed to the shadow treatment and to whatever efforts would be required to raise their survey scores. Dr. Greenwald conducted before and after patient surveys to measure progress, using the question "Would you recommend a friend or family member to this doctor's care?" as the basic indicator.

"We found that after the shadow intervention, two-thirds of the physicians raised their survey score by at least four percentage points," Dr. Greenwald says, "which we considered to be a statistically significant improvement because it lifted the doctors from the bottom quintile – where they had been stuck – at least to the next highest quintile. In some cases, the doctors' score jumped two or three quintiles!

"The techniques emphasized during the shadow encounters are now part of our orientation program for newly arrived physicians, as well as part of an ongoing program of continuous improvement for all lower-scoring physicians to raise 'OK' to 'great' and low outliers to at least 'average.'"

Team incentive program

To a physician, a new patient means more money; to an employee, every new patient means more work. When your employees hear that you're making a new push toward growing your practice, they can't be blamed for asking, "What's in it for me?"

There *can* be something in it for every member of your team and, come to think of it, there should be. Just about every high-scoring practice we know has found a way to reward everyone – physicians, supervisors, and staff – for achieving patient satisfaction improvement goals and promoting teamwork at the same time.

Here's how it works:

1. **Create teams** – A very small practice probably cannot divide itself into teams; but if you have more than six doctors, you should be able to create teams – perhaps by practice site, pod, or even specialty. The most logical approach is to consider how you account for your business performance. For example, if your monthly financial review examines revenue per physician, you might consider that each physician heads a team. If your doctors share certain staff, you might divide the practice by pod or department.

2. **Establish team goals** – You can set the same goal for all teams. For example, to reach the 75th percentile of the database for Question F1 ("Your overall satisfaction with our practice"). Or, you might choose several questions from the patient survey; for example, selected questions from Sections B and D (the logic is that doctors and employees have control over those scores, whereas questions from Sections A and C depend on the overall performance of the practice).

3. **Decide the rewards** – Stipulate an amount of money that every member of the team will earn if the goal is met. For example, if you use Question F1, you might set an award of $100 for every member of the team if the goal is achieved. If you select individual questions from Sections B and D, you might pay $20 per question. (Some practices also offer a bonus for high-scoring teams; for example, if a team achieves a score equal to the 90th percentile of the benchmarking database, the award is increased by some amount to reflect the top-level results.)

4. **Publish the results** – The key to a system based on team rewards is to let everyone know what each team has earned as the result of their efforts to reach or exceed the goals. Publishing the awards becomes an incentive for low-scoring teams to improve: "If they can do it, why can't we?"

The team reward strategy reverses the normal dynamic of using survey scores to improve your ability to attract and retain patients. Instead of traditional speech-making and arm-twisting by the leadership team, the burden for improvement is transferred to the people on the firing line – the physicians, supervisors, and staff members whose performance determines the success of the practice.

One office manager noted, "My doctors won't be motivated by a couple hundred dollars!" We disagree, for two reasons. One, physicians are among the most competitive professionals on earth; they hate to be ranked at the bottom of anyone's curve and seeing that others are out-performing their team is motivation enough for most of them. Two, even if physicians are not motivated by the relatively small dollar amounts of your incentive system, the team approach creates a subtle peer pressure to excel – it's difficult for even the crustiest physician to resist the frown on a nurse's face if she thinks *he* is the reason why *she* didn't get the money!

Please also notice that in nearly every discussion in this book, we keep returning to the patient survey as the ultimate measurement of success. There are good reasons why: Patient feedback is the best indicator of the marketing strengths and weaknesses of your practice, and a formal survey is the best tool for measuring them. Further, using quantified survey data gives everyone both a numerical measurement of your current "report card" and a basis for setting numerical goals that everyone can accept and strive to reach.

Each of the three momentum strategies in this chapter has been proven effective in small and large medical practices. Consider them as more than suggestions; if you can get support for making personnel rounds, help for low-scoring physicians, and a reward system based on team performance, the momentum of your Customer Service Initiative will have a life of its own.

Afterword

"The reward of a thing well done
is to have done it."

RALPH WALDO EMERSON

Some years ago a man – whose name is long since forgotten by the authors – was being interviewed on PBS. He was 93 years old. The subject was his life's biggest accomplishment. He had organized an immense clean-up of New York harbor in preparation for construction of the Verrazano Bridge – a daunting task which nearly every "authority" had claimed could not be done.

"How in the world were you able to do it?" asked the interviewer.

The man paused, then spoke, slowly and with great care in choosing his words. "It's the difference between optimists and pessimists," he said.

"Pessimists have well-prepared arguments why a thing cannot be done. They base their negativity on solid facts. Their objections make sense. And they are nearly always right.

"Optimists, on the other hand, usually have weak arguments, often based on faulty research and wishes rather than facts. Their ideas are often poorly expressed, and unconvincing. And, very often, they're wrong.

"But pessimists do not make progress."

Building a culture of customer service can be like that. People can challenge the validity of your service assessment. They can produce all kinds of well-founded reasons why service is impossible to deliver in a constantly changing environment where workloads and interruptions can't be predicted. They can vote "yes" and behave "no." They can claim that patients have unreasonable demands that can't be satisfied.

They may be right. Listen politely, but don't let them stop you. Orchestrating the ever-shifting dynamics of a medical practice is a noble challenge, and a big one. It's worth a life's effort.

You have our immense respect. And our best wishes.

End Notes

1. Mayo Clinic Proc, March 2006. Please note that technical expertise was not among the frequently mentioned attributes (which makes sense because most patients don't know how to judge the quality of the medical care they receive).

2. The MGMA-Sullivan/Luallin Patient Survey Program[SM] maintains the largest current-year ambulatory database in health care. The national database is built from more than 400 patient surveys each year and contains more than 300,000 individual patient responses. For a copy of the survey form, or more information on calculating beta coefficients using step-wise regression, contact the authors at inquiry@sullivan-luallin.com.

3. For descriptions of age categories and characteristics we're indebted to Mr. Cam Marston, internationally recognized speaker and consultant, and president of Marston Communications (P.O. Box 9687, Charlotte, NC 28299). For more information or to schedule a presentation for your group, Cam can be reached at 704.374.1413 or cam@marstoncomm.com.

4. The "Clinician and Group Survey" was designed by the CAHPS Consortium, which is the research arm of the Agency for Healthcare Research and Quality (AHRQ); part of its mission is to lobby for a standard survey instrument to measure the performance of all medical groups in the country. You can keep track of this government project by logging on to www.cahps.org.

5. Rensis Likert (b. 1903 - d. 1981) was an economist and sociologist who specialized in research in the social sciences, developing procedures and methods for studying people's attitudes and the variables that influence them. One product of his work was the creation of what would become the most widely used scale for attitude measurement, the Likert scale. In most applications the scale's values range from 1 to 5; the midpoint of the scale is reserved to reflect an undecided position. Likert-scale responses are tabulated and a statistical procedure is applied to determine the relative significance of each response.

6. The origin of this criterion is partly scientific. In Continuous Quality Improvement (CQI), for example, the task of improving work processes has a better chance if the process is "stable." The criterion for determining stability is if a minimum of 30 data points (observations) can be plotted within two standard deviations of the mean. In that case, the work process is said to be stable, which means that variation is nonrandom, i.e., "just part of the process itself" (Deming et al., 1988). The randomness of the data points also means that if you were to take 30 more observations, there's a good chance (95 percent probability) that they, too, would fall within the limits of a "stable" work process.

7. You may have heard of the "95-percent confidence level." The 95 percent level comes from academic publications, where a conclusion has to have at least a 95 percent chance of being true to be considered worth telling people about – it can't be considered proven, but *it is probably better to act as if it were true rather than false.*

8. As this book goes to press, the survey results for Avera/Avera McGreevy Clinic are not yet available. If you'd like to know what John Healy and his colleagues achieved, please contact the authors at 619-283-8988 after April 1, 2007.

Appendices

CLIENT NAME
Provider Name

Dear Patient: Our goal is to provide comfort, convenience, and satisfaction as well as the very best medical care to all our patients. We'd like to know how you feel about our medical services, our patient-handling systems, and our physicians and staff members. Your comments will help us evaluate our operations to ensure that we are truly responsive to your needs. Thank you for your help.

PLEASE RATE THE FOLLOWING:

	Excellent	Very Good	Good	Fair	Poor	Does Not Apply
A. YOUR APPOINTMENT:						
1. Ease of making appointments by phone	5	4	3	2	1	N/A
2. Appointment available within a reasonable amount of time	5	4	3	2	1	N/A
3. Getting care for illness/injury as soon as you wanted it	5	4	3	2	1	N/A
4. Getting after-hours care when you needed it	5	4	3	2	1	N/A
5. The efficiency of the check-in process	5	4	3	2	1	N/A
6. Waiting time in the reception area	5	4	3	2	1	N/A
7. Waiting time in the exam room	5	4	3	2	1	N/A
8. Keeping you informed if your appointment time was delayed	5	4	3	2	1	N/A
9. Ease of getting a referral when you needed one	5	4	3	2	1	N/A
B. OUR STAFF:						
1. The courtesy of the person who took your call	5	4	3	2	1	N/A
2. The friendliness and courtesy of the receptionist	5	4	3	2	1	N/A
3. The caring concern of our nurses/medical assistants	5	4	3	2	1	N/A
4. The helpfulness of the people who assisted you with billing or insurance	5	4	3	2	1	N/A
5. The professionalism of our lab or X-ray staff	5	4	3	2	1	N/A
C. OUR COMMUNICATION WITH YOU:						
1. Your phone calls answered promptly	5	4	3	2	1	N/A
2. Getting advice or help when needed during regular office hours	5	4	3	2	1	N/A
3. Explanation of your procedure (if applicable)	5	4	3	2	1	N/A
4. Your test results reported in a reasonable amount of time	5	4	3	2	1	N/A
5. Effectiveness of our health information materials	5	4	3	2	1	N/A
6. Our ability to return your calls in a timely manner	5	4	3	2	1	N/A
7. Your ability to contact us after hours	5	4	3	2	1	N/A
8. Your ability to obtain prescription refills by phone	5	4	3	2	1	N/A

Form: 1234A Provider: BQ Site: AL Specialty: S 04

PLEASE COMPLETE THE OTHER SIDE

	Excellent	Very Good	Good	Fair	Poor	Does Not Apply
D. YOUR VISIT WITH THE PROVIDER: (Doctor, Physician Assistant, Nurse Practitioner)						
1. Willingness to listen carefully to you	5	4	3	2	1	N/A
2. Taking time to answer your questions	5	4	3	2	1	N/A
3. Amount of time spent with you	5	4	3	2	1	N/A
4. Explaining things in a way you could understand	5	4	3	2	1	N/A
5. Instructions regarding medication/follow-up care	5	4	3	2	1	N/A
6. The thoroughness of the examination	5	4	3	2	1	N/A
7. Advice given to you on ways to stay healthy	5	4	3	2	1	N/A
E. OUR FACILITY:						
1. Hours of operation convenient for you	5	4	3	2	1	N/A
2. Overall comfort	5	4	3	2	1	N/A
3. Adequate parking	5	4	3	2	1	N/A
4. Signage and directions easy to follow	5	4	3	2	1	N/A
F. YOUR OVERALL SATISFACTION WITH:						
1. Our practice	5	4	3	2	1	N/A
2. The quality of your medical care	5	4	3	2	1	N/A
3. Overall rating of care from your provider or nurse	5	4	3	2	1	N/A

	Definitely Yes	Probably Yes	Don't Know	Probably Not	Definitely Not
4. Would you recommend the provider to others?	5	4	3	2	1

IF NO, PLEASE TELL US WHY: _____

_____

IF THERE IS ANY WAY WE CAN IMPROVE OUR SERVICES TO YOU, PLEASE TELL US ABOUT IT:

_____

_____

SOME INFORMATION ABOUT YOU:

GENDER		YOUR AGE		ARE YOU	
Male	1	Under 18	1	A new patient	1
Female	2	18–30	2	A returning patient	2
		31–40	3		
		41–50	4		
		51–64	5		
		65+	6		

Thanks very much for your help!

PATIENT
SURVEY
NETWORK™

SUPERCARE MEDICAL GROUP
Summary Report

September 2006

Supercare Medical Group
Summary Report
PATIENT SURVEY September 2006

Sample Size: n = 6,240

	Excellent	Very Good	Good	Fair	Poor
A. YOUR APPOINTMENT:					
1. Ease of making appointments by phone	55.1%	27.0%	10.8%	4.7%	2.4%
2. Appointment available within a reasonable amount of time	50.9%	27.5%	12.8%	6.0%	2.8%
3. Getting care for illness/injury as soon as you wanted it	54.8%	26.2%	10.8%	5.2%	3.0%
4. Getting after-hours care when you needed it	50.4%	25.6%	12.9%	4.9%	6.3%
5. The efficiency of the check-in process	56.0%	29.4%	10.7%	2.7%	1.2%
6. Waiting time in the reception area	42.0%	31.3%	16.2%	6.6%	3.7%
7. Waiting time in the exam room	41.4%	32.5%	16.4%	6.5%	3.3%
8. Keeping you informed if your appointment time was delayed	45.2%	25.7%	13.4%	7.3%	8.4%
9. Ease of getting a referral when you needed one	61.8%	23.4%	9.1%	3.6%	2.1%
B. OUR STAFF:					
1. The courtesy of the person who took your call	59.0%	25.8%	10.1%	3.4%	1.7%
2. The friendliness and courtesy of the receptionist	60.1%	24.9%	9.6%	3.6%	1.8%
3. The caring concern of our nurses/medical assistants	61.9%	24.5%	9.2%	3.1%	1.3%
4. The helpfulness of the people who assisted you with billing or insurance	58.8%	26.4%	10.0%	3.1%	1.5%
5. The professionalism of our lab or X-ray staff	57.5%	29.5%	10.3%	1.8%	0.9%
C. OUR COMMUNICATION WITH YOU:					
1. Your phone calls answered promptly	46.5%	29.9%	13.7%	5.5%	4.4%
2. Getting advice or help when needed during regular office hours	50.0%	28.7%	12.3%	5.5%	3.4%
3. Explanation of your procedure (if applicable)	57.6%	27.9%	10.0%	2.7%	1.8%
4. Your test results reported in a reasonable amount of time	49.8%	29.4%	12.5%	4.5%	3.8%
5. Effectiveness of our health information materials	49.0%	31.7%	14.2%	3.6%	1.5%
6. Our ability to return your calls in a timely manner	44.5%	28.5%	15.6%	6.0%	5.4%
7. Your ability to contact us after hours	45.8%	25.5%	14.1%	6.7%	7.8%
8. Your ability to obtain prescription refills by phone	56.9%	25.1%	11.5%	3.7%	2.9%
D. YOUR VISIT WITH THE PROVIDER:					
(Doctor, Physician Assistant, Nurse Practitioner)					
1. Willingness to listen carefully to you	69.4%	20.1%	6.6%	2.6%	1.4%
2. Taking time to answer your questions	69.3%	19.7%	6.7%	2.8%	1.5%
3. Amount of time spent with you	60.0%	23.5%	10.3%	4.3%	1.9%
4. Explaining things in a way you could understand	67.0%	21.6%	7.9%	2.5%	1.0%
5. Instructions regarding medication/follow-up care	64.2%	22.9%	8.5%	2.9%	1.5%
6. The thoroughness of the examination	62.1%	23.0%	9.6%	3.4%	2.0%
7. Advice given to you on ways to stay healthy	59.4%	24.4%	10.3%	3.4%	2.5%
E. OUR FACILITY:					
1. Hours of operation convenient for you	52.0%	30.1%	12.9%	3.5%	1.5%
2. Overall comfort	52.7%	30.5%	12.4%	3.4%	1.0%
3. Adequate parking	46.6%	26.3%	16.5%	7.0%	3.6%
4. Signage and directions easy to follow	53.6%	28.6%	14.4%	2.9%	0.6%
F. YOUR OVERALL SATISFACTION WITH:					
1. Our practice	61.5%	25.2%	8.8%	2.8%	1.7%
2. The quality of your medical care	64.7%	23.3%	7.9%	2.7%	1.4%
3. Overall rating of care from your provider or nurse	67.3%	21.2%	7.1%	2.7%	1.6%

	Definitely Yes	Probably Yes	Don't Know	Probably No	Definitely No
4. Would you recommend the provider to others?	76.1%	15.6%	3.5%	2.7%	2.2%

AGE						ARE YOU A		GENDER	
Under 18	18–30	31–40	41–50	51–64	65+	New Patient	Returning	Male	Female
2.5%	4.5%	7.4%	13.3%	25.7%	46.7%	7.1%	92.9%	38.4%	61.6%

Supercare Medical Group
Summary Report
Mean Score Benchmarking Comparison

Sample Size: 6,240   Database Size: n= 153,506   Multi-Specialty w/PCPs

A. YOUR APPOINTMENT

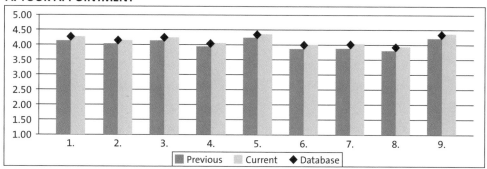

	Previous	Current	Database
1. Ease of making appointments by phone	4.15	4.28	4.29
2. Appointment available within a reasonable amount of time	4.02	4.18	4.22
3. Getting care for illness/injury as soon as you wanted it	4.12	4.25	4.27
4. Getting after-hours care when you needed it	3.96	4.09	4.06
5. The efficiency of the check-in process	4.25	4.36	4.34
6. Waiting time in the reception area	3.87	4.01	3.93
7. Waiting time in the exam room	3.88	4.02	3.90
8. Keeping you informed if your appointment time was delayed	3.80	3.92	3.83
9. Ease of getting a referral when you needed one	4.24	4.39	4.33

B. OUR STAFF

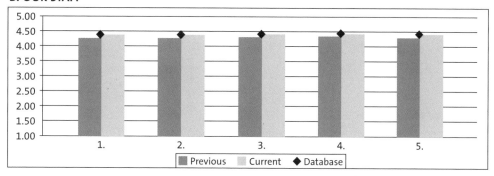

	Previous	Current	Database
1. The courtesy of the person who took your call	4.28	4.37	4.40
2. The friendliness and courtesy of the receptionist	4.30	4.38	4.41
3. The caring concern of our nurses/medical assistants	4.34	4.43	4.45
4. The helpfulness of the people who assisted you with billing or insurance	4.27	4.38	4.31
5. The professionalism of our lab or X-ray staff	4.27	4.41	4.36

Supercare Medical Group
Summary Report
Mean Score Benchmarking Comparison
Sample Size: 6,240   Database Size: n= 153,506   Multi-Specialty w/PCPs

C. OUR COMMUNICATION WITH YOU

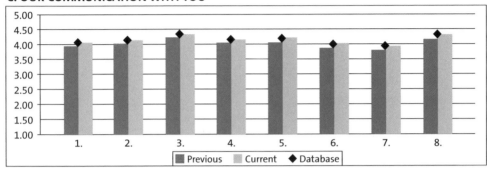

	Previous	Current	Database
1. Your phone calls answered promptly	3.94	4.08	4.06
2. Getting advice or help when needed during regular office hours	4.02	4.16	4.15
3. Explanation of your procedure (if applicable)	4.25	4.37	4.34
4. Your test results reported in a reasonable amount of time	4.03	4.17	4.13
5. Effectiveness of our health information materials	4.09	4.23	4.18
6. Our ability to return your calls in a timely manner	3.87	4.01	4.02
7. Your ability to contact us after hours	3.80	3.95	3.91
8. Your ability to obtain prescription refills by phone	4.17	4.29	4.21

D. YOUR VISIT WITH THE PROVIDER

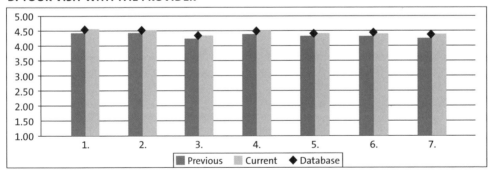

	Previous	Current	Database
1. Willingness to listen carefully to you	4.46	4.53	4.56
2. Taking time to answer your questions	4.45	4.52	4.55
3. Amount of time spent with you	4.26	4.35	4.40
4. Explaining things in a way you could understand	4.41	4.51	4.52
5. Instructions regarding medication/follow-up care	4.37	4.45	4.48
6. The thoroughness of the examination	4.31	4.40	4.44
7. Advice given to you on ways to stay healthy	4.27	4.35	4.39

Supercare Medical Group
Summary Report

Mean Score Benchmarking Comparison

Sample Size: 6,240   Database Size: n= 153,506   Multi-Specialty w/PCPs

E. OUR FACILITY

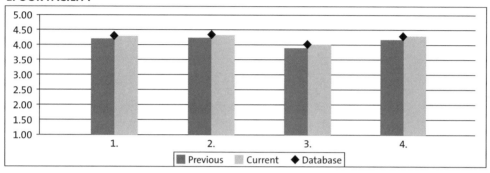

	Previous	Current	Database
1. Hours of operation convenient for you	4.18	4.28	4.27
2. Overall comfort	4.20	4.31	4.32
3. Adequate parking	3.89	4.05	4.11
4. Signage and directions easy to follow	4.16	4.32	4.29

F. YOUR OVERALL SATISFACTION WITH:

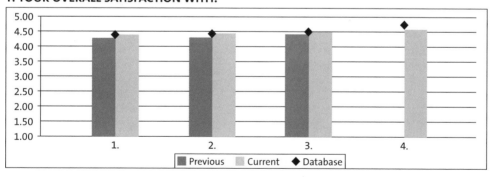

	Previous	Current	Database
1. Our practice	4.33	4.42	4.43
2. The quality of your medical care	4.38	4.47	4.49
3. Overall rating of care from your provider or nurse	4.42	4.50	4.54
4. Would you recommend the provider to others?	N/A	4.61	4.75

★ ★ ★ ★ ★

90th PERCENTILE MEAN COMPARISON

	Client Mean Score	Client Percentile Rank against the Database	Multi-Specialty & PCP Database 90th Percentile	Multi-Specialty & PCP Database Score
A1. Ease of making appointments by phone	4.17	23.0%	4.73	4.32
A2. Appointment available within a reasonable amount of time	3.93	13.8%	4.63	4.22
A3. Getting care for illness/injury as soon as you wanted it	4.04	16.0%	4.65	4.27
A4. Getting after-hours care when you needed it	3.96	24.8%	4.57	4.10
A5. The efficiency of the check-in process	4.38	49.0%	4.68	4.36
A6. Waiting time in the reception area	4.03	54.2%	4.43	3.96
A7. Waiting time in the exam room	4.02	54.9%	4.42	3.96
A8. Keeping you informed if your appointment time was delayed	3.89	47.0%	4.46	3.87
A9. Ease of getting a referral when you needed one	4.21	23.6%	4.68	4.34
B1. The courtesy of the person who took your call	4.41	45.0%	4.77	4.42
B2. The friendliness and courtesy of the receptionist	4.50	55.8%	4.78	4.44
B3. The caring concern of our nurses/medical assistants	4.44	39.7%	4.77	4.46
B4. The helpfulness of the people who assisted you with billing or insurance	4.35	47.1%	4.69	4.33
B5. The professionalism of our X-ray staff	4.33	31.8%	4.72	4.39
C1. Your phone calls answered promptly	3.91	22.6%	4.65	4.11
C2. Getting advice or help when needed during office hours	4.06	29.4%	4.67	4.19
C3. Explanation of your procedure (if applicable)	4.32	37.0%	4.71	4.37
C4. Your test results reported in a reasonable amount of time	4.02	24.6%	4.58	4.18
C5. Effectiveness of our health information materials	4.10	29.2%	4.61	4.21
C6. Our ability to return your calls in a timely manner	3.87	23.4%	4.56	4.06
C7. Your ability to contact us after hours	3.81	29.6%	4.54	3.96
C8. Your ability to obtain prescription refills by phone	4.10	24.2%	4.65	4.23
D1. Willingness to listen carefully to you	4.58	48.4%	4.78	4.55
D2. Taking time to answer your questions	4.57	47.1%	4.78	4.54
D3. Amount of time spent with you	4.37	38.4%	4.70	4.39
D4. Explaining things in a way you could understand	4.54	48.6%	4.76	4.51
D5. Instructions regarding medication/follow-up care	4.50	50.2%	4.73	4.47
D6. The thoroughness of the examination	4.47	47.7%	4.73	4.45
D7. Advice given to you on ways to stay healthy	4.42	49.3%	4.69	4.39
E1. Hours of operation convenient for you	4.29	45.5%	4.60	4.30
E2. Overall comfort	4.31	40.3%	4.67	4.34
E3. Adequate parking	3.99	30.4%	4.65	4.10
E4. Signage and directions easy to follow	4.23	37.4%	4.62	4.28
F1. Our practice	4.41	38.0%	4.76	4.44
F2. The quality of your medical care	4.46	33.0%	4.78	4.50
F3. Overall rating of care from your provider or nurse	4.54	40.4%	4.80	4.55
F4. Would you recommend the provider to others?	4.71	21.8%	4.93	4.76

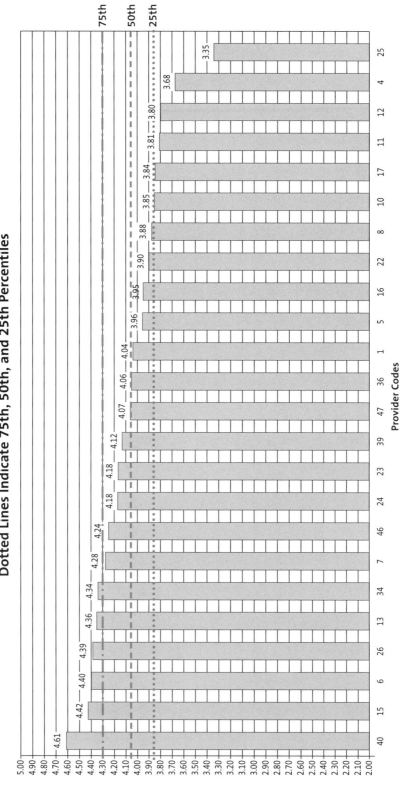

SUPERCARE MEDICAL GROUP – PROVIDER RANKING BY QUARTILE
Average of Section D – "Your Visit With Your Doctor"
Dotted Lines Indicate 75th, 50th, and 25th Percentiles

MYSTERY PATIENT CHECKLIST

Evaluator _____

Doctor _____

Appt date/time _____

Patient name _____

Reason for appt _____

Practice site _____

PRE-VISIT CHECKLIST: Date/time of call _____   Number of rings _____

1. OPERATOR:

—Greeting: Gave location   Y   N

—Gave name   Y   N

—Said "May I help you?"   Y   N

—Sounded rushed   Y   N

—Voice tone: Friendly   Neutral   Cool   Unfriendly

2. IF PLACED ON HOLD:

—Asked if you could hold   Y   N

—Waited for answer   Y   N

—Hold time _____ seconds/minutes

—Said "Thank you for holding."   Y   N

3. IF TRANSFERRED TO SCHEDULER:

—Number of rings _____

—Greeting: Gave location   Y   N

—Gave name   Y   N

—"May I help you?"   Y   N

—Sounded rushed   Y   N

—Stay on line until call answered   Y   N

4. QUESTIONS ASKED BY SCHEDULER:

—Used patient name during call   Y   N   NA

—Asked about health coverage   Y   N   NA

—Asked about presenting problem   Y   N   NA

—Asked for phone number/address   Y   N   NA

—Asked what medications taking   Y   N   NA

—Asked if new/established patient   Y   N   NA

—Asked for date of birth   Y   N   NA

—Offered appointment options   Y   N   NA

—Was preferred day/time honored?   Y   N   NA

5. INFORMATION PROVIDED BY SCHEDULER:

—Alerted to expect forms in mail   Y   N   NA

—Payment arrangements   Y   N   NA

—Asked about special needs   Y   N   NA

—Gave directions to office/how to register   Y   N   NA

—Other

—Voice tone: Friendly   Neutral   Cool   Unfriendly

OVERALL RATING OF PRE-VISIT EXPERIENCE:

4	3	2	1
Very satisfied with all aspects. Would definitely return/refer.	Somewhat satisfied with aspects. Would probably return/refer.	Somewhat dissatisfied with aspects. Would probably not return/refer.	Very dissatisfied with aspects. Would definitely not return/refer.

COMMENTS ABOUT PRE-VISIT EXPERIENCE:

1. _____

2. _____

3. _____

4. _____

5. _____

CHECK-IN AND ROOMING:

1. RECEPTION AREA:

–Directions and signage clear	Y	N
–Clean/orderly	Y	N
–Reading materials neat/current	Y	N
–Furniture clean/comfortable	Y	N
–Ambient noise pleasant	Y	N
–Restrooms clean	Y	N

2. CHECK-IN/REGISTRATION
RECEPTION:

–If no line, greeted you within 3 seconds	Y	N
–If a line, acknowledged you	Y	N
–Said "May I help you?" (and smiled)	Y	N
–If on the phone, eye contact/signal	Y	N
–Professional appearance	Y	N
–Cash payment collected	Y	N
–Given directions where to wait	Y	N
–Name badge	Y	N
–Informed of doctor's status	Y	N
–Demeanor: Friendly Disinterested Unfriendly		

3. NURSE/MEDICAL ASSISTANT:

–Called patient by last name	Y	N
–Waited for patient to get to doorway	Y	N
–Introduced self	Y	N
–Wore name badge	Y	N
–Acknowledged new patient status	Y	N
–Explained what was happening (If appl)	Y	N
–Said when MD would enter exam room	Y	N
–Kept patient apprised of status	Y	N
–Maintained confidentiality	Y	N
–Asked if patient needed anything	Y	N
–Asked if patient had other questions	Y	N
–Explained appointment was over	Y	N
–Demeanor: Friendly Disinterested Unfriendly		

4. LENGTH OF WAIT IN RECEPTION:

< 15 min 16–30 min 31–45 min 45+ min

5. LENGTH OF WAIT IN EXAM ROOM:

< 5 min 6–15 min 16–30 min 30+ min

OVERALL RATING OF CHECK-IN AND ROOMING:

4	3	2	1
Very satisfied with all aspects. Would definitely return/refer.	Somewhat satisfied with aspects. Would probably return/refer.	Somewhat dissatisfied with aspects. Would probably not return/refer.	Very dissatisfied with aspects. Would definitely not return/refer.

COMMENTS ABOUT CHECK-IN AND ROOMING:

1. _____

2. _____

3. _____

4. _____

5. _____

VISIT WITH PROVIDER:

1. ENTRY – ESTABLISHING RAPPORT:

–Knocked on exam room door   Y   N

–Friendly greeting, handshake   Y   N

–Used your name   Y   N

–Made small talk   Y   N

2. ELICITING INFORMATION:

–Allowed you to finish describing problem   Y   N

–Seated, maintained eye contact   Y   N

–Used active listening techniques   Y   N

–Faced you (not chart)   Y   N

–Asked if you had any other issues   Y   N

3. EXAMINATION:

–Thoroughness   Y   N

–Explained what s/he was doing   Y   N

–Gave results as s/he went along   Y   N

4. EDUCATING THE PATIENT:

–Explained things in understandable way   Y   N

–Used layperson's language   Y   N

–Used visuals/models where needed   Y   N

–Gave written information/instructions   Y   N

–Confirmed your understanding   Y   N

5. ENDING THE VISIT:

–Asked (again) about any other issues   Y   N

–Warm, friendly handshake   Y   N

–Parting comment   Y   N

OVERALL RATING OF VISIT WITH PROVIDER:

4	3	2	1
Very satisfied with all aspects. Would definitely return/refer.	Somewhat satisfied with aspects. Would probably return/refer.	Somewhat dissatisfied with aspects. Would probably not return/refer.	Very dissatisfied with aspects. Would definitely not return/refer.

COMMENTS ABOUT CHECK-IN AND ROOMING:

1. _____
2. _____
3. _____
4. _____
5. _____

CHECK-OUT

–Received check-out instructions   Y   N
–Receptionist made parting comment   Y   N

Demeanor of staff: Friendly   Disinterested   Unfriendly

OVERALL COMMENTS ABOUT VISIT:

_____
_____
_____

THE CARE GROUP
STANDARDS OF EXCELLENCE

A. PATIENT RELATIONS

1. Treat patients with respect and professionalism.

   – Arrive within 15 minutes of the first appointment, unless unavoidably detained for professional reasons. Make every effort to stay on schedule throughout the day.

   – In the exam room, greet patients cordially, introduce yourself (apologize if you're late), and address them using their last names.

   – In communicating with patients, use appropriate body language (sit at eye level when appropriate). Make eye contact.

   – When covering for colleagues, treat their patients as your own.

2. Communicate effectively with patients.

   – Assume the role of educator, teaching patients and family members about the illness. But remember, some patients have more medical education and knowledge than others. Don't talk down to those who already know what you're talking about.

   – Listen with compassion. Acknowledge and try to resolve their concerns. Empathize in times of grieving. Give priority to their complaints about our office.

   – Help patients set realistic expectations for return calls, test results, and other information.

   – Use nontechnical language.

   – Do not criticize a colleague, referring physician, or Care Group staff member within patients' hearing range.

   – Explain that patients may be seen by other TCG physicians, who also provide excellent care. Introduce the "weekend" doctor by name on daily rounds.

3. Make yourself available to patients.

   – Ensure that your patient care schedule realistically reflects your work schedule. Avoid unnecessary interruptions. Delegate tasks to staff members to maximize your productivity.

   – Be available for daily review of the hospital plan and patient progress, by phone or in person, with patients and family members.

B. STAFF RELATIONS

1. Show staff members that they are appreciated and respected.

   – Be a role model for staff in demonstrating your commitment to patient satisfaction.

   – Be a team leader. Know your care team or pod employees by name. Recognize the importance of major events in their lives and their individual problems.

   – Take the initiative in thanking staff members for their efforts. Pass along patient compliments along with complaints.

   – Offer constructive feedback or reprimands in a private, nonthreatening manner.

   – Educate staff members without condescension.

   – Encourage staff to contribute new ideas and suggestions.

   – Do not blame staff members for scheduling or system problems. Focus on solutions to process problems.

2. Support the efforts of supervisors to manage staff members.

   – Do not undermine supervisors. Discuss your problems and concerns in private. Support supervisors' decisions regarding your clinical staff.

C. COLLEAGUE RELATIONS

1. Treat TCG colleagues with respect.

   – Recognize the contributions of other TCG doctors to the success of our group.

   – Apologize for mistakes or misunderstandings.

2. Communicate and cooperate with colleagues.

   – Provide honest, constructive feedback in the spirit of improving patient care and satisfaction, and be willing to accept constructive feedback from others.

   – Deal with clinical and personnel responsibility issues in a physician-to-physician manner – not through employee intermediaries.

   – Be enthusiastically willing to see other doctors' patients.

   – Answer pages in a timely fashion; make every effort to take physician calls immediately.

– Return phone calls from physicians as quickly as possible. Minimize delegating the phone response to staff members.

3. Communicate and cooperate with referring physicians.

– Include the referring physician as part of the team.

– Define and communicate expectations for the consult. In urgent cases, alert physicians personally before sending the patient. Provide appropriate work-up information.

– Communicate effectively. Send patient status report letters within 48 hours. For urgent consults, call primary care physicians yourself within 24 hours. For routine consults, report progress within 72 hours.

– Be available for urgent consults, even at the end of the day.

– Consult with referring doctors before sending patients to another specialist.

– Call at least two referring physicians each day.

D. PROFESSIONALISM

1. Contribute to the positive image and success of our group.

– Dress professionally in the office and at the hospital.

– Maintain patient confidentiality by keeping sensitive discussions from being overheard.

– Avoid alcohol and any drugs/medications that could impair your judgment when on call, at the clinic, and at the hospital.

– Attend partnership meetings. Familiarize yourself in advance with agenda items, and be prepared to contribute to the discussions.

– Be willing to participate on committees.

Six-Steps to Customer Satisfaction — From Patient Survey to Action Plan

By Kevin W. Sullivan

Practice leaders understand the need to be the provider of choice in their service area. However, a difference exists between practices that achieve best in market prominence and those whose results fall short of expectations. This article summarizes the experience of small and large medical groups and identifies the strategies that mark providers of choice in competitive markets nationwide.

System vs. sermon

In health care, you can manage performance two ways. Clinical, technical and procedural expectations are carefully defined, closely managed and not optional. Service expectations are too often loosely defined, managed through in-service pep-talks, and left to the discretion of physicians and employees.

As a consequence, performance varies among departments and practice sites – particularly when medical professionals go on autopilot in the face of heavier workloads, demanding patients, lean staffing and limited resources.

Many Medical Group Management Association members use a more formal and businesslike process for measuring their strengths and weaknesses and convert the findings into workable action plans that produce immediate improvement and ongoing results.

Figure II.B.6 illustrates a six-step process used by best-practice organizations – single- and multispecialty groups as well as independent practice association provider networks – to analyze strengths and weaknesses, define service standards, monitor performance, hold people accountable for results and recognize top contributors.

Step 1 – Service Assessment

To build a business plan to protect your existing revenue base and generate new market share, you need to take the first step and know how customers perceive your service strengths and weaknesses.

Use a patient survey as your tool to obtain feedback from a large number of people who offer a customer's perspective on how it feels to access your services. All questions should have a positive statistical correlation with overall satisfaction, which means that any increase in scores will improve your market position.

More detailed information can be found in mystery patient visits in which an experienced observer can spot strengths and weaknesses in specific performance areas that affect patient loyalty and referrals.

Finally, surveying and interviewing your inside customers – board mem-

Figure II.B.6	THE SIX-STEP CUSTOMER SERVICE INITIATIVE

1. Conduct a baseline service assessment
  – patient satisfaction survey
  – "mystery" patient visits
  – physician, supervisor, staff surveys
  – key-leader interviews

2. Leadership involvement (buy-in and objectives)
  – review service assessment
  – set quantifiable goals
  – form Customer Service Committee
  – develop Action Plan

3. Develop service standards
  – develop customer-centered performance standards
  – incorporate into job descriptions
  – integrate into the performance appraisal process

4. Conduct training workshops
  – Physicians and mid-levels
  – Managers and supervisors
  – Clinical and support staff

5. Track performance (benchmark)
  – "dashboard" monitoring/reporting
  – monitor progress
  – provide support to departments

6. Momentum strategy
  – ongoing communication program
  – "booster" meetings
  – recognize top performers

Figure II.B.7	PATIENT SURVEY FINDINGS			
		Mean Score	Percentile Ranking	90th Percentile
	A1. Ease of making appointments by phone	4.56	67.7%	4.76
	A2. Appointment available in a reasonable amount of time	4.47	73.0%	4.70
	A3. The efficiency of the check-in process	4.54	60.2%	4.73
	A4. Waiting time in the reception area	4.08	57.6%	4.47
	A5. Waiting time in the exam room	4.06	60.6%	4.44
	A6. Keeping you informed if appointment time was delayed	4.10	53.1%	4.58

bers, physicians, managers and staff – not only produces essential feedback, but also builds stronger support for your action plan among people who are consulted beforehand.

Step 2 – Leadership involvement

Every provider needs to perform as if customer satisfaction is the key to protecting the existing revenue base and generating new market share. Furthermore, research has proven that satisfied patients don't litigate, and that happy employees surpass those who clock in for a paycheck. In terms of medical quality, there is a direct correlation between patients who are satisfied with provider communication and compliance with treatment plans, which leads to improved medical outcomes.

Convene a meeting of board members, physicians and managers – all the people who will be involved in implementing the action plan. Review the findings of the service assessment and ask the group to help set improvement priorities for the coming year. This is also a good time to formalize responsibility for coordinating the implementation process through a customer service committee comprised of physicians, managers and employees – with at least one board member in an ex-officio capacity.

Bristol Park Medical Group (Costa Mesa CA) took a unique approach to building its Customer Service action plan. In a half-day meeting, 44 Board and committee members, Medical

Directors, Administration, and department heads reviewed the assessment, set priorities and goals, and assigned responsibilities to designated task groups. The leadership team reviewed progress at every monthly partner meeting, and modified strategies as needed.

You can use patient survey findings to set improvement priorities. Figure II.B.7 shows how survey scores can be viewed in terms of their percentage rankings. You can use the percentile rankings to determine which areas to address as well as the score you'll need to rank in the top 10 percent of the database.

In Figure II.B.7, the mean score for question A1 ranks at the 67.7 percentile of the benchmark database. A score of 4.76 must be reached to rank in the top 10 percent of the database.

In taking this approach, your practice will have quantifiable goals to measure progress. With specific goals, the customer service committee can now brainstorm strategies for raising the score from 4.56 to 4.76 by the next time you survey your patients.

Step 3 – Service standards

Service performance needs the same careful definition as clinical and procedural criteria – not only for employees but also for physicians and nonphysician providers who are part of the delivered product. Successful practices connect improving scores on specific survey questions with job descriptions and annual performance appraisals.

Physician standards should reflect the four phases of the patient encounter: establishing rapport, eliciting information, educating the patient and ensuring compliance. The standards should also include issues related to staff relations, peer relations and partnership or professional criteria.

Employees must address customer service as a priority, not an option or an ideal to be pursued only on good days. Rather, exceeding customer expectations must become a part of the practice's mission and values – as important to professionals as medical quality and technical expertise. Staff performance standards should include making a great first impression, using appropriate telephone etiquette, handling patient complaints and creating a team environment within and among departments (See Figure II.B.8).

Rockwood Clinic (Spokane WA) made its service standards the centerpiece of physician seminars, manager development, and staff workshops. To ensure the effectiveness of the training, the Customer Service Committee began a series of self-directed "mystery patient" visits, and engaged consultants to conduct "shadow coaching" encounters for low-scoring physicians.

Step 4 – Skills training

Once you publish and understand the standards, conduct training seminars to enable everyone in your practice to meet or exceed the standards. As an example, patient surveys usu-

Figure II.B.8	CUSTOMER SERVICE STANDARD (Staff)

MAKE A GREAT FIRST IMPRESSION

1. Acknowledge patients immediately; use eye contact and smile

2. Let patients know of expected delays; keep them informed of their status

3. Use the patient's last name until you sense using first names is appropriate

4. Use layperson's language whenever possible

5. Be an active listener; pay attention to what the patient is saying

6. Be helpful to patients who need help finding their way around the facility

7. Give clear directions; answer all questions with patience and professional concern

8. Reassure anxious patients; ask what you can do to make things easier

9. Conclude with a friendly "thank you"

ally contain a question about the amount of time the physician spends with a patient. Your doctors need to understand that answers to this question have nothing to do with actual minutes spent in the exam room. Top ratings go to physicians who know the techniques that make patients feel that the limited encounter time was well spent. Body language, eye contact, active listening and other validating behaviors produce satisfied patients and high survey scores.

Similarly, staff members can learn and practice techniques that enhance patient satisfaction. When rooming the patient, for example, medical assistants get high marks when they make congenial small talk and use the patient's name.

Once you've trained front- and back-office people in customer-pleasing techniques, a special effort should be made to improve the leadership skills of those responsible for medical and staff management. A formal manager training program will emphasize skills for team building, conflict resolution, correcting unsatisfactory performance, preparing and conducting objective performance reviews and other key subjects.

Step 5 – Tracking mechanisms

Establish tracking mechanisms to measure progress and keep customer service at the top of everyone's agenda. Use follow-up patient surveys, referrer and insider surveys, requests for records transfer, exit interviews of departing physicians and staff members, and number and source of complaints. Develop monthly reports and reserve a portion of each partner-management meeting to review them.

Step 6 – Momentum strategy

The final step in your action plan involves momentum – promotional activities that keep customer service in the minds of every member of the practice and recognition programs that reward top performers. Small and large practices can use a variety of strategies to encourage top-level performance by rewarding those who excel at customer satisfaction.

Some practices establish programs in which service stars receive public recognition; others install bonus formulas in which high-scores on customer surveys equate to monetary awards. In any case, these programs help practice managers reinforce their commitment to customer satisfaction.

Enhance momentum by publishing the results of regular patient surveys

and referring-physician surveys for single-specialty practices that depend on referrals for a major portion of new patients.

In addition, many best practice groups maintain a continuing schedule of mystery patient assessments, where trained observers use first-hand observations to look beyond the survey data, identify specific performance areas and recommend practical strategies for improving the survey scores.

Bright Medical Associates (Whittier CA) uses monthly reports from "mystery patient" visits and telephone calls to help physician-manager teams spot deficiencies in daily operations or performance, and develop fast-track action plans to improve customer satisfaction.

Many practices use shadow coaching as an effective strategy to improve customer satisfaction. A trained consultant dons a lab coat, poses as a writer doing a story, and follows the physician through a day's encounters – after which the low-scoring doctor receives direct, one-on-one feedback on how he/she interacted with patients seen during the day.

Putting it all together

The six-step process closes the disconnect that often exists between leadership plans and front-line performance. It produces a cultural change in meeting and exceeding customers' service expectations. The process emphasizes that service is not an option and holds each member of the practice accountable for making internal and external customers feel valued and important.

Your practice benefits by gaining greater patient loyalty and more patient referrals.

SOURCE: *Performance and Practices of Successful Medical Groups: 2004 Report Based on 2003 Data.* Reprinted with permission from the Medical Group Management Association, 104 Inverness Terrace East, Englewood, Colorado 80112. www.mgma.com.

COPY FOR INSTRUCTIONS TO MYSTERY PATIENTS

Dear (name),

Thank you for agreeing to be part of our continuing mystery patient program.

You're taking part in a very important program — we need your feedback to measure how well our services respond to your needs. Our doctors and staff know about this program, and everyone at our practice is enthusiastic about improving our services in any way we can.

1. Please review the items on the checklist prior to your appointment.

2. Bring the checklist to your appointment, but don't let anyone know that you're a "mystery patient" or see what you're doing.

3. Complete the checklist as soon as possible, and please feel free to add any comments (e.g., the name of someone who was particularly helpful to you).

4. Return the checklist in the enclosed reply envelope within two days after your visit.

As a token of our appreciation, please accept the enclosed gift certificate, with our compliments.

And thanks again for helping. You are our best source of information about where we shine and what needs polishing!

Sincerely,

/s/

Medical Director

SUPERCARE MEDICAL GROUP
VISIT CHECKLIST
(Please circle the most appropriate answer)

A. WHEN YOU CALLED FOR THIS APPOINTMENT:

Did the person who took your call sound friendly?	YES	NO	N/A
If you were placed on hold, were you asked if you could hold?	YES	NO	N/A
Did the person thank you for holding?	YES	NO	N/A
Did the person sound rushed?	YES	NO	N/A

B. WHEN YOU ARRIVED FOR YOUR APPOINTMENT:

Were you greeted quickly?	YES	NO	N/A
Was the receptionist friendly and courteous?	YES	NO	N/A
Was the receptionist wearing a name badge?	YES	NO	N/A
Did the receptionist use your name?	YES	NO	N/A
While you were waiting, did we keep you aware of your status?	YES	NO	N/A
Was the reception area clean and comfortable?	YES	NO	N/A

C. WHEN YOU WERE CALLED TO THE EXAM ROOM:

Did the nurse/medical assistant introduce him/herself?	YES	NO	N/A
Did the nurse/medical assistant use your last name?	YES	NO	N/A
Was the nurse/medical assistant wearing a name badge?	YES	NO	N/A
In the exam room, did we keep you aware of your status?	YES	NO	N/A
Do you feel that we were careful about your confidentiality?	YES	NO	N/A
Did you hear any inappropriate side chatter among our staff?	YES	NO	N/A

D. DURING YOUR VISIT WITH THE PROVIDER:

Did the provider listen carefully to you?	YES	NO	N/A
Did the provider spend enough time with you?	YES	NO	N/A
Did the provider take time to answer all your questions?	YES	NO	N/A
Did the provider explain things in a way you could understand?	YES	NO	N/A
Did the provider tell you about ways to stay healthy?	YES	NO	N/A

E. WHEN YOUR VISIT WAS OVER:

Did someone advise you that the visit was over?	YES	NO	N/A
Did someone ask if you had any other questions?	YES	NO	N/A
Did someone say good-bye to you?	YES	NO	N/A

F. AND THINKING ABOUT YOUR TOTAL EXPERIENCE:

Did we make you feel like a valued and important patient?	YES	NO	N/A
Do you want to come back to us the next time you need care?	YES	NO	N/A
Would you refer a family member or friend to our practice?	YES	NO	N/A

Thanks very much for your help! Please return this survey in the reply envelope within two days.

TECHNIQUES FOR RAISING PATIENT SURVEY SCORES

Patient satisfaction surveys are designed to provide feedback on a practice's strengths and limitations. Reading a survey report and learning where you shine in the eyes of your patients is a pleasure-filled, enjoyable task. Not so much fun, though, is getting the negative feedback that points out your weaknesses. It can be particularly frustrating if you're fresh out of ideas for improvement.

The following strategies, listed by question as they appear on the MGMA-Sullivan/Luallin patient survey, have been used by practices nationwide to raise their survey scores.

SECTION A: YOUR APPOINTMENT

Q1. Ease of making appointments by telephone

Call your office (anonymously) at different times of the day and different days of the week to make an appointment. Check how many buttons need to be pushed before connecting to a live person. Learn what questions the scheduler asks prior to making the appointment for you. What you discover from your "mystery patient" encounter will help you to improve the process for real patients.

Q2. & 3. Availability of appointments

a)　Add mid-level providers and instruct your appointment staff to use positive adjectives in recommending that the patient see a mid-level provider. (Too often a staff member will ask the caller, "Do you mind seeing the PA?" Or worse, "If you want to get in today, you'll have to see the nurse practitioner.")

b)　Instruct staff members to offer the patient another physician who has an opening in the schedule. (Frequently an appointment scheduler on "autopilot" will respond to a caller, "Sorry, he's all booked up" and go to the next call.)

c)　Add a "walk-in" department to handle nonemergent urgent care needs of patients.

Q4. Getting after-hours care when you need it

Make sure patients know the number of the closest Urgent Care Center associated with your practice. One practice has a printed pad with important after-hours phone numbers for patients to call for care. (See

Appendix I for a sample of the patient information form used by Dr. Scott Shiffman, Bristol Park Medical Group.)

Q5. The efficiency of the check-in process

a) Review your procedure for checking in patients. Much of the information needed from new patients can be elicited by telephone while setting the appointment. Many practices send a welcome letter, practice brochure, and the patient information form in advance so that patients can complete it at home. Some practices are taking advantage of technology and people's willingness to use self-registration kiosks in their offices.

b) For patients who balk at having to verify their address, phone number, and insurance information during each visit, instead of having the receptionist ask, "Has anything changed with your information?", suggest that s/he say, "You're still at [address], right? And your insurance is still [health insurance company name], right?" One practice displays a prominent sign that reads, "WE ASK BECAUSE WE CARE."

c) New patients deserve special treatment. Typically, receptionists will say, "I see you're a new patient ... here, fill out these forms." Better to have a new patient identified so that every member of the practice can make the welcome warmer. (See the "heart" paper clip in Appendix J.)

Q6. Waiting time in reception area

a) Check the scheduling system to make sure it's realistic. Elderly patients need more time than younger ones. Complete physicals and new patient visits, which often run long, are better scheduled in the afternoon.

b) Discuss the scheduling process with physicians and staff members; ask for improvement ideas.

c) Provide cookbooks and 3x5 cards with your logo for patients to use for copying recipes.

d) Provide coupons for snack at a nearby shop. (One ENT practice gives coupons to a nearby yogurt shop if the physician is running more than 20 minutes behind.)

e) Provide pagers to caregivers who are waiting for patients who are undergoing minor procedures, such as cataracts or colonoscopies.

f)   Have a table with a jigsaw puzzle to keep waiting patients occupied.

g)   Provide attractive stationery for patients to write letters; offer to stamp and mail them.

h)   Encourage the use of a "Confidential Patient Agenda," a blank piece of paper on which patients list questions and issues they have for the physician. The nurse reviews the questions ahead of time and can answer any appropriate ones. The physician can use the list to control the time in the exam room more efficiently.

i)   Post a sign assuring patients that the doctor will spend ample time with them. (See Appendix K for a sample sign.)

Q7. Waiting in exam room

a)   Provide up-to-date magazines. Hang a bulletin board and post thank-you letters and pictures of staff and their families.

b)   Provide shawls in exam rooms for OB/GYN patients, who generally must disrobe prior to their exam.

c)   Provide a status report every 5 to 7 minutes, letting patients know their position in the queue.

d)   Remind patients to alert the doctor if they need extra services. (See Appendix L for a sample sign to hang in your exam rooms.)

Q8. Keeping patients informed if their appointment time is delayed

Nurses and receptionists need to work as a team. Nurses should alert receptionists to the physician's timeliness or tardiness so that the receptionist can let arriving patients know the approximate time they will be called back to the exam room. Patients should have the option to reschedule if necessary.

Q9. Ease of getting a referral

a)   If you are a primary care practice, be sure that your physicians are portrayed as coordinators of patient care, capable of handling all but the most acute patient problems. Use the patient brochure to describe the process by which your practice arranges for specialist care on the occasions when it may be needed. Tell patients up front the typical turnaround time for securing a referral or authorization. (Increase your estimate by a few days to exceed patient expectations.)

b)   Check that the members of your practice who are responsible for arranging the referral understand the procedures, and encourage them to explain the steps they're taking on the patient's behalf.

SECTION B: OUR STAFF

The service protocols and scripts presented in Chapter Six give you the fundamentals for helping your staff members make patients feel valued and important. Further, we've observed several techniques used by administrators and office managers, as follows:

Q1. The courtesy of the person who took your call

a)   Hold a "hallway huddle" with employees who regularly interact with patients on the telephone. Review the service protocol "Be a telephone superstar" and reinforce the importance of Star-Studded phone etiquette.

b)   Make regular phone calls to various extensions in your practice; listen carefully for voice tones and phrases.

c)   Place a small mirror at each phone station and suggest that staff members look at themselves while talking on the telephone. Advise everyone to smile as they speak with callers.

Q2. The friendliness and courtesy of the receptionist

a)   Hold a "hallway huddle" with your receptionists. Review the service protocol "Make a great first impression" and reinforce the importance of Star-Studded Service.

b)   Ask your physicians to enter the practice by the front door at least twice each week. Stress the value of saying "Good morning" to receptionists and engaging them in brief discussions regarding techniques for welcoming patients and caregivers.

Q3. The caring concern of our nurses and medical assistants

Hold a "hallway huddle" with your nurses and medical assistants. Review the service protocol "Room patients with caring professionalism" and "Say good-bye when patients leave the practice" and reinforce the importance of Star-Studded Service.

Q4. The helpfulness of the people who assisted you with billing or insurance

Hold a "hallway huddle" with employees who regularly interact with patients on matters of billing and insurance. Make sure everyone understands that their job includes helping patients who need assistance in understanding the procedures or completing forms.

Q5. The professionalism of our lab or X-ray staff

Hold a "hallway huddle" with your technicians and technologists. Review all service standards and moderate a discussion of techniques for interacting with patients during lab or X-ray testing.

SECTION C: OUR COMMUNICATION WITH YOU

Q1. Phone calls handled promptly

Develop customized telephone message pads that call takers need to write a minimum of information. Set patient expectations by establishing specified call-back times. Establish a separate phone line for referring physicians. Establish a separate phone line for pharmacy *renewals* (distinguish between refills that can be completed by the pharmacy directly and prescription renewals that require physician authorization). Engage a phone nurse just to handle calls (particularly in pediatrics).

Q2. Availability of medical information/advice by telephone during office hours

In more mature managed care markets, health plans have established "Nurse on Call" services. Check in your area to see if your practice is eligible for offering this service. For routine calls, be certain that patients' questions are answered while they are at the office. Encourage nurses, medical assistants, and providers to ask, "Do you have any questions?" or "Did you get all of your questions answered?" before patients exit your practice.

Before they leave the practice, ensure that patients know what their diagnosis is, what the next steps are in their treatment plan, what their medications are and how to take them, and so on. This will reduce telephone calls and open lines for unanticipated medical questions.

Q3. Explanation of procedures

Physicians need to be aware of the terminology they use to describe upcoming tests and procedures. Patients process and retain information more effectively when doctors use three-dimensional teaching models or illustrated pamphlets. Many practices provide information through educational videos, which patients can borrow and return prior to their procedures. Other providers refer patients to Web sites that have fuller descriptions of their procedures.

Q4. Reporting test results

One of the key factors affecting patient satisfaction and referrals is providing quick notification of test results. Consider using "standard paragraphs" in a personal computer to speed note-writing. Monitor the performance of the ancillary test facilities you use, and make sure they know that timely turnaround is important to you. Further, put a flagging device on the chart (such as a bright-colored "post-it" note or a plastic clothespin) to note important test results that need to be called to patients. Further, let patients know when to expect the results to be reported to them. If you know that the turnaround time for a lab test result is five working days, tell the patient it will be at least seven working days. In that way, you build in time for unexpected delays; if you respond to the patient sooner than seven days, s/he will think you're wonderful!

Q5. Effectiveness of health information materials

When providing printed materials to patients, personalize the handout with some written notation pertinent to the patient. Get information from disease societies or patient education companies such as Krames Communications. Use computer-generated materials. Get information from medical societies and academies (such as ACOG, ACC, or ASA).

Q6. Doctor returning calls in a timely manner

Many patients who complain that physicians do not return phone calls quickly have unwarranted expectations regarding these calls. It's helpful if the individual taking the call advises the patient when to expect the physician's return call (such as at the end of the day or early the next morning). Further, the call-back system works most smoothly when the doctor has set call-back times; this policy can be communicated to patients through a newsletter, memo, or insert in billing statements.

Q7. Availability after hours

Conduct a test of your answering service by calling after hours to learn how responsive and courteous the operators are. Also, monitor the call schedule, and ask the physicians how it needs to be modified if there is a problem.

Q8. Obtaining prescription refills by phone

Distinguish between prescription refills and prescription renewals. The number of refills authorized by the provider is noted on the medicine container, and refills typically do not need a physician's permission. The patient should be encouraged to call the pharmacy directly for refills. Renewals, however, do need provider authorization, and a separate telephone line for these will facilitate obtaining them. Be sure in the renewal telephone message to tell the patient how long it will take for your office to authorize the prescription before calling it in to the pharmacy. Some patients have unrealistic expectations regarding turnaround times because no one has educated them on what they should expect.

SECTION D: YOUR VISIT WITH THE PROVIDER

Q1. Doctor willingness to listen

Be seated after a friendly "hello" and make eye contact. Allow patients to "tell their stories" and respond with an empathy statement such as "I'm sorry to hear that" or "That's got to be tough." Acknowledge patients' instincts about their illness. Read their chart before entering the exam room. When patients answer questions, look at them for a few seconds before looking down to write in the chart.

Q2. Doctor taking time to answer questions

Before ending the exam, ask, "What else can I tell you about (your problem)?" At the end of the exam, say, "If you think of something else, give us a call; Sue (the nurse) can answer your questions."

Q3. Spending time with the patient

Time is not always the issue, but rather how the physician uses the time s/he has with the patient. (Often the most popular physician is the busiest. As a result, this doctor spends *less* time per encounter than other providers.) Be seated after you have performed the physical portion of the exam. Use relaxed body language (sit back in the chair, cross your legs, put the cap on your pen, and look directly at the patient). Patients need to perceive that their physician cares about them. These feelings can be conveyed in a brief amount of time if the doctor uses empathy statements and appropriate body language.

Q4. Explaining things in a way you could understand

Treat the patient as a partner in decision-making by describing treatment options in nontechnical terms. Recommend the course of treatment you would take if you were the patient, and use three-dimensional models to explain diagnoses when appropriate.

Q5. Instructions regarding medication and follow-up care

Many practices provide printed materials that contain instructions for follow-up care. A special touch is to type the patient's name on a label and affix it to the folder.

Q6. Thoroughness of the exam

Many times patients have an expectation of what constitutes a thorough examination. This includes appropriate touching (checking glands, for example). While the doctor performs the exam, s/he needs to describe what is being done and why. At the end of the encounter, during the "wrap up," the doctor should briefly review for the patient what every step of the examination indicated.

Q7. Advice on ways to stay healthy

With HEDIS measures and Pay-for-Performance campaigns in the spotlight, most physicians today know that they need to emphasize healthy lifestyles and screening tests. Some practices actually have checklists in the patient file that the doctor must sign indicating that s/he has discussed these important issues with patients.

SECTION E: OUR FACILITY

Q1. Hours of operation

Consider expanding your office hours to include early morning or late afternoon appointments. To determine which hours patients prefer, conduct another short patient survey to obtain feedback from your customers.

Q2. Overall comfort

Sometimes patient perceptions of "comfort" differ from those of people who work in the practice every day (and who may not notice that the carpeting is becoming over-worn, the walls need cleaning, and so on). For an objective look at your practice from an "overall comfort" standpoint, consider a "Mystery Patient" assessment – a process in which an experienced evaluator goes through an actual visit (from appointment telephone scheduling to the last step in the encounter). The "Mystery Patient's" report will contain many valuable observations and recommendations for making improvements to ensure the overall comfort of patients and visitors.

Q3. Adequate parking

There's not much you can do about the lack of parking spaces near your practice. However, you can certainly let patients know that you sympathize with their problem. Sometimes you can suggest that a mid-day or afternoon appointment might make it easier to find a parking space. We believe the most important way to demonstrate your empathy is for your physicians and staff to park at the far end of the lot, leaving the closest spaces for patients.

Q4. Signage and directions

Criticism of signage often comes from first-time or elderly patients who have difficulty finding your office – people you definitely don't want to antagonize! Consider asking someone who doesn't work in your practice "go through the motions" of parking, entering your building, consulting the directory, and finding their way to your front door. Make changes accordingly. If your location is particularly difficult to find – for example, tucked away in a corner of a large hospital or office building – consider sending a map to help first-time patients find their way.

SECTION F: YOUR OVERALL SATISFACTION

Q1. With our practice

Patients' overall satisfaction with your practice is a cumulative sense of how they were treated from their first telephone encounter through their departure. This score is heavily dependent on a positive experience with all other aspects of your practice.

Q2. With the quality of your medical care

Patients are typically unable to evaluate the appropriateness or clinical quality of the care physician's delivery. They judge medical quality often on the service they receive. In addition, providers who hope to score high in this category are most successful when they describe what they are doing or prescribing and why. Finally, setting realistic patient expectations regarding outcomes decreases the likelihood of anger or distress at a less-than-optimum result.

Q3. Your overall rating of care from provider or nurse

See advice provided in previous Sections B and D.

BRISTOL PARK
M E D I C A L

SCOTT SHIFFMAN, M.D.

Follow-up Instructions

PATIENT NAME: _____

MRN # _____

INSTRUCTIONS: _____

_____

_____

_____

APPOINTMENT: ☐ CALL WHEN NEEDED

☐ SCHEDULE: ___ DAYS ___ WEEKS ___ MONTHS

REASON FOR APPOINTMENT: _____

Appointment Scheduled: _____ **Time:** _____

TO REACH US AFTER HOURS:

URGENT CARE CENTERS: Fountain Valley   (714) 549-1300
Mission Viejo   (949) 582-2002
Hours: 9am–9pm weekdays and 9am–5pm weekends/holidays

TELEPHONE ADVICE NURSE LINE: To speak with an Advice Nurse, simply call your doctor's office and select the Advice Nurse Line from the phone menu.
Available 24 hours a day / 7 days a week

For more information visit us on the web at www.bristolparkmed.com
29472 Avenida De Las Banderas
Rancho Santa Margarita, CA 92688
(949) 459-9968

REC-0003   7/04

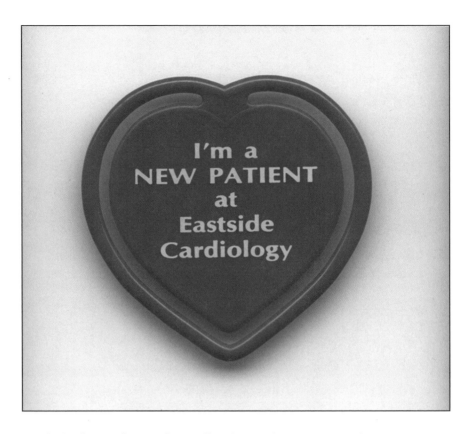

A colorful "HEART" paperclip is affixed to each new patient chart to designate their "new" status.

Thank you for your patience. Dr. (name) will soon be providing you the same level of personal and professional care he is presently providing to another patient.

Posted in the reception area of a Concord, Calif., physician practice.

Need a

- **Work note?**
- **School excuse?**
- **Prescription refill?**

Don't forget to ask the doctor before you leave the exam room!

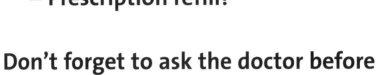

Index